PICKY EATER

Joan,
Thanks for reading,
+ hope you enjoy!

♡ always,
jessica rothem

PICKY EATER

32 INSIGHTS, LESSONS, AND GUIDELINES WHEN THEY "HAVEN'T GROWN OUT OF IT"

JESSICA ROHRER

NEW DEGREE PRESS

PICKY EATER

32 Insights, Lessons, and Guidelines when they "haven't grown out of it"

ISBN   978-1-64137-190-2 *Paperback*

            978-1-64137-191-9 *Ebook*

CONTENTS

INTRODUCTION   9

HOW TO USE THIS BOOK   21

PART 1.   **WHAT IS PICKY EATING?**   **25**

CHAPTER 1.   WHEN IT ALL CHANGED   27

CHAPTER 2.   MOM OF A PICKY EATER   37

CHAPTER 3.   SAFE VS. STUBBORN   53

CHAPTER 4.   FOOD CONSCIOUS   63

RECIPE   CRISPY HOME FRIES   71

PART 2.   **EXPOSURE AND INVOLVEMENT**   **73**

CHAPTER 5.   EXPOSURE HELPS   75

CHAPTER 6.   INVOLVE THEM EARLY ON!   83

CHAPTER 7.   PLAY WITH YOUR FOOD   93

CHAPTER 8.   SEE, SMELL AND TOUCH FIRST   99

CHAPTER 9.   REPEAT, REPEAT, REPEAT   109

RECIPE   SWEET POTATO FRIES   117

PART 3.   **WHAT TO DO AND MODELING**   **119**

CHAPTER 10. STUMBLING UPON FOOD CHAINING   121

CHAPTER 11. SET THE TABLE FOR SUCCESS   129

CHAPTER 12. MODELING MATTERS   139

CHAPTER 13. RELAX AND DESTRESS   147

RECIPE   HASH BROWNS   153

PART 4.   **LEARN ABOUT FOOD AND COOKING**   **155**

CHAPTER 14. LEARN AT THE FARMERS MARKET   157

CHAPTER 15. TEACH YOURSELF THE BASICS   165

CHAPTER 16. START WHERE YOU ARE   173

CHAPTER 17. QUALITY AND SOURCE AFFECT TASTE   179

CHAPTER 18. LEARN WHAT GOOD IS AND DEMAND IT   185

RECIPE   POTATO PANCAKES   193

PART 5.   **OUR RELATIONSHIPS WITH FOOD**   **195**

CHAPTER 19. FROM BIRTH   197

CHAPTER 20. WHAT IS "HEALTHY"?   207

CHAPTER 21. FOOD IS MEDICINE   217

CHAPTER 22. EMOTIONAL FOOD   229

CHAPTER 23. FOOD BELIEFS   239

RECIPE   BAKED POTATO   247

PART 6.   **WHAT NOT TO DO**   **251**

CHAPTER 24. DON'T BLAME YOURSELF OR OTHERS   253

CHAPTER 25. DON'T FORCE IT   261

CHAPTER 26. DON'T FALL FOR THE DIET MINDSET   269

CHAPTER 27. DON'T FORGET YOUR GOAL   279

RECIPE   MASHED POTATOES   287

PART 7.   **AWARENESS AND CHANGE**   **289**

CHAPTER 28. WRITE IT DOWN   291

CHAPTER 29. START WITH ONE SMALL STEP!   301

CHAPTER 30. ONE CHANGE CAN LEAD TO MANY!   311

CHAPTER 31. CHANGE YOURSELF FIRST   323

CHAPTER 32. FIND A REASON TO CHANGE   333

RECIPE   GNOCCHI   341

CONCLUSION   345

ACKNOWLEDGEMENT   349

RECIPES   351

CITATIONS   363

INTRODUCTION

———

For more than twenty-nine years I was a picky eater and was told I would "grow out of it."

Except I didn't.

I started as a picky eating child…became a picky eating teenager…then a picky eating high schooler… then a picky eating college student…until finally I was a picky eating adult out in the "real world" who still hadn't "grown out of it"!

I'm here to let the millions of people just like me know it's okay if you're picky or haven't "grown out of it" and it IS possible to change.

✶✶

This book is designed to offer a new and fresh take on picky eating.

While there are certainly challenges to being, raising, living with or caring for a picky eater, we will take a look at the science and psychology of the picky eater and provide a framework for the extremely picky eater and those around him or her to live in perfect harmony and make change possible.

I've come to discover that the traditional approach for alleviating picky eating in toddlers doesn't always work for children, teenagers or adults that have developed a food phobia. The advice being given to parents and families right now is missing a few pieces of the puzzle. A lot of additional information is available and there are strategies that can be used to vastly improve a picky eater's diet and relationship with food—both when they are young and when they are older. My most surprising discovery is just how many people out there have felt the same way I have. Millions of us identify with "picky eating" to varying degrees and I'm not as alone in this struggle as I thought.

**

There is a stigma against picky eating—that preferences for certain foods means we are ungrateful, unhealthy or just being stubborn.

"You're being rude. You should eat what you're offered."

"If you weren't so picky you'd be healthier."

"You're just being stubborn. You could try it if you wanted."

But for most picky eaters it was ingrained in our subconscious or became a learned behavior very early on.

Google "picky eater" and you'll be greeted with millions of hits and articles that offer tips to parents for "how to get your child to eat."

It's no wonder picky eating in adults and teenagers hasn't been identified for what it really is and gets swept into the stubborn, fussy eating, toddler phase.

But what is "picky eating" anyway and is there really such a thing as "normal eating"?

The National Institutes of Health are the first to admit that part of the challenge is, "There is no single widely accepted definition of picky eating."

Picky eating is more of a "feeding difficulty" than some of the potentially more serious disorders. Therefore, picky eating is sometimes described as "disordered eating" in contrast to an "eating disorder." But what's the difference and where does the blurred line from one begin and the other end?

An "eating disorder" is a mental illness characterized by abnormal eating habits (that may involve restriction, bingeing and purging) to the detriment of a person's health alongside an unhealthy preoccupation with food, weight, shape or body image.

However, "disordered eating" refers to a wide range of irregular eating behaviors that do not warrant a diagnosis of a specific eating disorder. Most picky eating among children falls under mild to moderate disordered eating and will resolve over time or with the support of an outpatient dietitian, therapist or pediatrician.[1]

Picky eating is generally defined as occurring in children who are a normal weight but consume an inadequate variety of foods through rejection of foods that may either be familiar or unfamiliar to them. Common characteristics include limitations in the variety of foods eaten, unwillingness to try new foods (food neophobia), and aberrant eating behaviors. Picky or fussy eating may

---

1   Eatingrecoverycenter.com. (2019). *Picky Eating vs. Disordered Eating (ARFID) Signs & Symptoms | Eating Recovery Center.* [online] Available at: https://www.eatingrecoverycenter.com/families/portal/resource-center/where-does-picky-eating-end-and-disordered-eating [Accessed 12 Jan. 2019].

include rejection of foods of a particular texture, consistency, color, or smell. Such food neophobia generally peaks between the second and sixth year of life, with a gradual reduction over time.[2]

**

However, what is taking place when picky eating does not naturally reduce over time. While much has been written about this conventional picky eating phase in toddlers and young children, extremely picky eating continuing into adulthood is a relatively new topic in the health profession. It didn't even have a name until 2013. Now the *Diagnostic and Statistical Manual of Mental Disorders* (DSM) has labeled picky eating in adults as Selective Eating Disorder (SED) or Avoidant Restrictive Food Intake Disorder (ARFID). The DSM previously lumped picky eaters into a classification of eating disorder "not otherwise specified," which was a catchall category for people who didn't meet the criteria for a major disorder. In fact, in a 2014 survey of 2,490 Canadian pediatricians, the Canadian Pediatric Surveillance Program, stated that 63 percent of pediatricians and pediatric subspecialists were unfamiliar

---

2 Norris, M., Spettigue, W. and Katzman, D. (2016). Update on eating disorders: current perspectives on avoidant/restrictive food intake disorder in children and youth. *Neuropsychiatric Disease and Treatment*, p.213.

with the diagnosis of SED or ARFID. Additionally, of those who suspected that a previous patient had SED or ARFID, 30 percent were found to have misdiagnosed that patient.

I'm not really sure how I feel about it having a name now; I never thought of myself as having an eating disorder growing up. I was just the girl who only ate PB&Js and french fries. Although, I will admit, I'm glad the name has brought more awareness to the subject and along with that more research and professionals who understand what it is and can help to treat it.

As I've been writing this book and starting to tell people about it, I've been shocked by the responses I've gotten. I keep finding people I've never met before in my life telling me how they currently are a picky eater or how they used to be a picky eater and understand what it is like—a friend of a friend who only orders plain chicken for dinner, the woman sitting next to me at a food summit, a coworker's aunt, a fellow author, a professor's daughter, a friend's little brother, an acquaintence at the market, a close friend's husband…the list goes on and on. My whole life I thought I was the only picky eater out there, and now I'm running into picky eaters of varying degrees constantly. We all have our food preferences and chances are we all know at least one friend or family member who is picky.

How many picky eaters are really out there and have tried to keep this secret just like I have? At present, few population studies have focused or reported on rates of SED or ARFID, which is not surprising given that it has only recently been identified and given a name. However, in a survey taken in January 2015 by Statista titled "Picky Eaters in the United States," 26 percent of responders said they consider themselves picky eaters.[3]

Among pediatric inpatient eating disorder programs the rates of SED or ARFID have ranged from 5 percent to 14 percent and as high as 22.5 percent in a pediatric eating disorder day treatment program. Studies have consistently demonstrated that, compared to those with anorexia or bulimia, SED or ARFID patients are younger, are more likely to be male, and are commonly diagnosed with other additional anxieties or medical symptoms.[4]

**

---

3   Statista. (2015). *Which of the following people, if any, do you consider to be picky eaters?*. [online] Available at: https://www.statista.com/statistics/426021/picky-eaters-in-the-united-states/ [Accessed 12 Jan. 2019].

4   Norris, M., Spettigue, W. and Katzman, D. (2016). Update on eating disorders: current perspectives on avoidant/restrictive food intake disorder in children and youth. *Neuropsychiatric Disease and Treatment*, p.213.

The truth is this book also represents my own journey to understand the stigma around picky eating and offer a new look at the science and psychology of picky eating and the food world. Personally, I've been through the challenge of being a picky eater since I was less than two years old and, after many years of struggling to change, was finally able to overcome my picky eating.

For a woman who often felt like she was being judged for her food preferences growing up, I've gone back and forth quite a bit on whether I was comfortable enough with my picky eating journey to put myself out there and tell my story. I've done everything I could for most of my life to hide my picky eating from people, to NOT talk about it, NOT make it a big deal, and pretend like I was "normal."

Yet, I wrote this book to let the whole world know how NOT normal I really am. There is no reason I couldn't just move on with my life now that I can try anything and eat everything and pretend like I never was a picky eater in the first place. I moved to a brand new city where no one knew I used to be a picky eater, so why bring it up? It's a lot of work to put into something I didn't really want most of the world to know about.

I mean… of all the things in the world for me to write about, I never in my wildest dreams thought I'd be writing a book about food!

The trouble is I kept coming back to the fact that I am so grateful and feel so lucky that I'm not a picky eater anymore and I can now eat anything! It's changed my entire life. Now I truly understand what "life-changing" means, but man was I scared. I had no idea if I would ever be able to reach the people who might benefit from this book. But was I really going to let my fear of others knowing about my picky-eating past hold me back from potentially helping another picky eater just like me embrace healthy eating habits?

I sat down and meditated, prayed, talked with friends and family and asked for guidance. The answer: if there was even a small chance I could help one person, I had to try.

The information my mom was provided by pediatricians, psychologists and psychiatrists when I was younger was usually misinformed or not very helpful. My picky eating was not identified for what it was. It wasn't just the conventional stage of fussy eating that toddlers go through, and so my phobia and anxiety grew worse as I got older instead of better. I can't help but be frustrated that there weren't more resources out there for me when I was a young girl as a picky eater or that there wasn't more guidance for my parents from the various health professionals they talked with to help my mom and dad. What if something could have been done about it and my life could have changed twenty years earlier if we had only known what to do?

**

Throughout this book, I've tried to assemble core insights and information to provide a more holistic and nonjudgmental view of picky eating.

This book is for anyone who is trying to help a picky eater or has ever struggled with their relationship with food. I wrote this for you whether you are:

- a picky eater like I was who hasn't "grown out of it" and so badly wants to change but doesn't know how
- an amazing mother, father, or loved one who knows and cares about a picky eater, or
- a nutritionist, psychologist, or medical professional who is passionate about helping each of us improve our health and relationships with food.

I want picky eaters and their loved ones to have somewhere to go to learn and understand picky eating. I want picky eaters to have someone to go to for advice and be able to talk about it. I want parents to know how their relationship with food is affecting not only their own health, but the health of their children as well. I want parents to improve their own relationships with food and help their children grow up with healthy and happy relationships with food. I want people to know that how we think about food can have a huge impact on our lives and health. Most importantly, I want picky eaters to know they are not alone. It is possible to change and many things can be done to help them start trying new foods.

After going through it on my own, I've been extremely curious and have done extensive research to figure out if there was a way I could help others apply the same process I did by diving into these questions:

- Why and how was I able to change?
- What are the common themes?
- What has worked for others?
- What good, helpful and proven advice is available?
- What made things worse?
- How does our attitude about food affect our health?

So relax, take a deep breath and get ready. We are going to answer those questions and so many others! You've taken the first step, which is always the hardest, by picking up this book and it only gets better from here. I can't wait to share this incredible journey with you!

HOW TO USE THIS BOOK

———

This book is organized around the following seven parts and themes for picky eaters *and* those close to picky eaters to understand more about our relationships with food.

- Part 1 – What Is Picky Eating?
- Part 2 – Exposure and Involvement
- Part 3 – What to Do and Modeling
- Part 4 – Learn about Food and Cooking
- Part 5 – Our Relationships with Food
- Part 6 – What Not to Do
- Part 7 – Awareness and Change

To help you navigate this book, I've outlined my suggestions for the parts you may want to focus on. I would suggest everyone take a look at part 1 to gain a broader understanding of what picky eating is. After that, please feel free to jump around to the sections that most spark your interest.

For the picky eater like me who hasn't "grown out of it" and is ready for change, I'd suggest focusing on the following chapters and sections:

- What Is Picky Eating?
- Exposure and Involvement
- What to Do and Modeling
- Learn about Food and Cooking
- Our Relationships with Food
- Awareness and Change

For the amazing loved one or medical professional who just wants the best for a picky eater in their life, check out:

- What Is Picky Eating?
- Exposure and Involvement
- What to Do and Modeling
- Our Relationships with Food
- What Not to Do
- Awareness and Change

At the end of each part of the book is a recipe with a different way to cook a potato, giving you the opportunity to explore some of the versatility of just one food. I liked the idea of learning more and expanding on different ways to eat a potato because I know how picky eaters love french fries (me included). They are such a crispy, salty and delicious snack. Exploring how to eat a potato in different ways has been really interesting for me because as a picky eater I was scared to try any other versions of a potato. Throughout the book we will learn seven different delicious ways to cook a potato. We will try slightly different tastes and different textures (crispy, crunchy, smooth, creamy and soft) and we will cook it various ways (baked, roasted, boiled, and fried). We start very simple, with easy to learn recipes and just a few basic ingredients that will increase in complexity throughout the book. Enjoy!

PART 1

WHAT IS PICKY EATING?

What is picky eating? When is it more than just conventional fussiness in toddlers? How and why is it different? Why do some people not grow out of it? This section is all about getting to know more about picky eating, starting with some of my personal journey. Then we'll dive into each of these questions and gain a better overall understanding for how to identify picky eating, discuss what it is like for picky eaters and their parents, and explore what medical professionals should know about picky eating.

CHAPTER 1

WHEN IT ALL CHANGED

———

My relationship with food has transformed from an "extremely picky eater" to a "foodie" who can try anything.

I've loved food…I've hated food.

I've been disgusted by it… and curious about it.

Fearful of it… and ashamed because of it.

I've been a picky eater ever since I can remember, and according to my parents I started spitting food back out and showing signs of extreme pickiness ever since I was thirteen months old.

The first question I usually get from people is, "What do you eat?"

My diet has mainly consisted of peanut butter and jelly (PB&J) sandwiches, grilled cheese, cheese quesadillas, french fries, popcorn, chips, crackers, cereal, apples, bananas and grapes for the majority of my life.

Next is usually a series of questions starting with, "What about... (fill in the blank)?"

The answer almost always was, "No."

No pasta, no meat (no bacon, no burgers, no chicken), no fish, no eggs, no rice, no vegetables, no beans, no salads, no pizza.

And yes I did just say no pizza! That is what my diet looked like for over twenty-nine years.

Logically, I could see no reason why I shouldn't be able to try what everyone else was eating, but every time I'd sit down to try a food, I would have intense anxiety, nervousness and fear. It was a very frustrating internal battle. I don't even know the number of times I told myself, "Look, everyone else is eating it and they are completely fine. What's wrong with you? Just eat it already! It won't kill you."

The problem was I just couldn't. My parents did everything they could when I was little to get me to try new foods but all of the doctors and psychologists always just said, "She is healthy. Don't worry about it. She's young. She'll grow out of it."

The thing is, I never grew out of it. It was challenging growing up in such a food-based culture with so many of our social activities revolving around food. Set lunches for school trips, pizza at birthday parties, dinner with work clients, going out on dates at nice restaurants, appetizers for happy hour, set menus at weddings and corporate conferences, and grabbing lunch with coworkers. Each and every one of these situations was a challenge for me. While all of my friends enjoyed a nice meal for our prom dinner, I had a roll with butter on it. Your plate just feels like this big glaring white spot, stark and empty while everyone else has full plates. People can't help but notice and ask questions. I so badly wanted to change. I wanted nothing more than to just be able to eat normal food like everyone else, but any attempts I made were a struggle and were not very successful. Any time I tried to eat something new, I'd get anxious, my palms would sweat, and I'd feel myself choking up.

However, my desire to change never went away. I continued occassionally trying on my own and created my picky eating blog in 2012 to record my progress and to hopefully inspire other picky eaters. I made some very small progress like going from vanilla ice cream to trying chocolate ice cream, but it wasn't until November 26, 2016 that I had a life-changing experience and the biggest breakthrough of my life.

The day before was Thanksgiving, and I discovered Felix Economakis and his online video therapy. I was living in Brussels, Belgium, at the time and he was located in London. This was the first Thanksgiving I hadn't spent with any of my family or friends, which was basically my most dreaded nightmare.

It's bad enough not eating normal food on a regular basis for dinner and social events, but it is downright awful on the most celebrated food day of the year. I loved to spend time with my family on Thanksgiving. It is one of my most cherished memories. The sound of football playing in the background while we all sit around the counter sharing a bottle of wine. Laughing all day while we prepped food and cooked all afternoon. But there it was, the sole focus of our entire day around food and spending an hour in the morning discussing all the amazing appetizers we would make and how this year we wanted to try out three separate stuffings instead of just two. I wanted to participate but felt like I couldn't and hated all the focus on food. It was the one day, more than any other day, in the year that highlighted just how different and weird I really was.

Now, living in Belgium, I wouldn't even be able to spend time with my family this year. Thankfully though, I made amazing friends in Belgium and one of my friends invited me over to her house for Thanksgiving with her family. They made me feel so welcome, were so kind, and I was so thankful for them that day. No one said a thing when all I put on my plate was some cornbread, cheese and crackers and eventually I was able to relax and enjoy the day with them. It meant so much to me.

Earlier that morning before heading to my friend's house for Thanksgiving dinner, I had researched Felix Economakis and read as many of the reviews and testimonials as I could. I discovered he had three therapy options: an online video therapy, online Skype sessions with him, and in person therapy sessions. Since I was in Belgium I figured I'd just start with the online videos and then schedule a follow up session if I thought his therapy might work for me.

I was extremely skeptical, so I didn't tell anyone that I was going to try it, including my family or friends. I didn't want to get anyone's hopes up, including my own, just to find out that it didn't work and was a big sham. But for the first time in my life, everything he was saying and wrote about picky eating made it seem like he actually understood what was going on. He identified it as selective eating disorder and I figured he might actually be able to help. What did I have to lose?

The day after Thanksgiving, November 26, I picked five new foods to try, as Felix advised, and prepared them for after my therapy session. I picked some REALLY out of the box foods that would be a stretch for me to try. I had raw carrots, green beans, chicken nuggets, a plain cheeseburger, and a Caesar salad.

These were currently in the "no way in hell" category of foods I'd ever be willing to try. I wasn't even eating rice or watermelon, no less trying meat like chicken or beef. The thought of trying a burger scared the crap out of me and just getting the food prepared ahead of time had me pretty anxious. The salad felt completely overwhelming with so many different components to it. I felt discouraged just looking at all of it, thinking there was no way I could try all of those different ingredients combined.

These foods were so challenging because there were so many different tastes and textures all going on at once. Not only does a cheeseburger have beef on it but it also has bread and cheese and lettuce and tomatoes and ketchup, each of these with their own unique tastes and textures. A salad felt overwhelming for the same reason. It had lettuce and chicken and croutons and cheese and carrots and a dressing. And these are usually just the start with any number of possible different ingredients. I couldn't even wrap my mind around trying lettuce no less all of these ingredients together at the same time.

I made a trip to McDonald's for the chicken nuggets, cheese-burger and salad, and then I peeled the carrots and cooked the green beans. It took me quite a while to prepare every-thing and figure out how to cook the green beans, but at last I had each new food sitting on the table in front of me.

Before starting the video therapy, I took a quick video on my computer of myself and described how I felt about try-ing these foods, like I'd seen some other people do online. I wanted to have before and after videos to show my family back home in case it actually worked. Then I sat down, took a deep breath and started Felix's online video therapy.

Something amazing, unreal, and truly life-changing hap-pened. After the video therapy I got up, walked over to the dining room table, sat down and took my first bite of a carrot. Then I took a bite of a green bean, took a bite of one of the chicken nuggets, took a bite of the cheeseburger and lastly tried some of the lettuce in the salad! I had willingly just tried five new foods I never would have dreamed of touching two days prior!

Felix's online video therapy takes you through a series of six videos. In the first few videos, he starts with an introduction and preparation. You participate in a few activities to guide your conscious and subconscious in a new direction and help remove the fear of trying something new. There is an optional hypnosis portion as well but it is not required for the therapy to work. Then there is a de-briefing section and the steps to actually try the new foods you have prepared.

I couldn't believe it. I was shocked. It was just one or two small bites of each, but it was so much more than I ever thought possible. Like I said, these were REALLY stretch foods for me. You can actually still see my before and after videos from that day posted on my blog. They are so awkward for me to watch now, but I love them as a reminder of how far I've come. It was incredible and I was thrilled.

There are no words to describe how long I hoped, dreamed and prayed for my picky eating to go away. For the first time in my life I was hopeful that maybe, just maybe, I wouldn't be weird and different anymore and could just eat normal food.

But I was still skeptical since there was some hypnosis involved I thought, "Well okay, we'll see if it still works tomorrow."

The next morning I decided I was going to try some of these foods again. I hopped on the bus and took it to the closest McDonald's to my house, which was off of the Chaussee d'Ixelles about ten minutes away. I went up to the counter to order and asked for chicken nuggets and a burger with American cheese and nothing else on it. Then I looked for as private a seat as I could find (which to be honest was not very private) and I sat down and for the second time in twenty-nine years tried a chicken nugget and a plain cheeseburger.

I completely burst into tears and just sat there and cried. I was still able to take a bite and swallow just like that! No fear, no anxiety, no dread, no reflux, no choking. I got quite a few weird looks but I didn't care. I was able to try new foods! That particular McDonald's will always have a special place in my heart because of that day. My life would never be the same.

But Felix's therapy wasn't some magic pill. I didn't all of a sudden love to eat everything. His therapy simply removed the overwhelming fear and anxiety tied to trying a bite of something new. I couldn't just sit down and eat an entire burger with all the fixings on it for dinner, but I could take one bite of a new food, which was a HUGE step. I didn't know after one bite whether I liked it or not, but I did know it would be possible to try a whole bunch of new foods that I never ever would have gone near in the past.

It took a lot of time, effort, and consistency to continue trying new foods, but I worked at it for the next two years and can eat anything now. Although there were times when I was tired of trying new things—tired of figuring out what to try next, tired of searching for it at the grocery store, tired of researching how to cook it and tired of actually cooking it all for just one or two bites.

As I'm sure we've all experienced, it takes time to meal plan, and trust me when I say it takes A LOT of time and effort to rebuild your entire diet. There were days when all I wanted was something familiar, and I would just have a grilled cheese for dinner. And that was completely okay. I needed a little break but that didn't mean I gave up. I was always ready to try new things again after a day or two. Real lasting change takes time and no one is perfect. But I was determined to change. I kept at it and am grateful every day that I can now try anything.

I would love for any picky eaters out there who have struggled like I have to know there is hope and help available! I wish I could have found out what my food phobia was and how to fix it years and years ago! For me it was truly a blessing.

Picky Points:

- Some picky eaters never "grow out of it" and become extremely picky eating adults with selective eating disorder (SED).
- Extremely picky eaters with SED want to change and eat "normal" food just like everyone else.
- It takes time and effort but it is possible to change if you are an extremely picky eater.

CHAPTER 2

MOM OF A PICKY EATER

———

"I devoted my life to being a mom. That's what I did, that was my choice, and I wanted to be the best at it. When I saw you weren't eating like other children, it was crushing for me. But I never thought of you as an abnormal kid." ~Mom

"It was frustrating.

It was confusing.

I felt guilty.

I was angry.

I was hurt and upset."

"What was really frustrating were the doctors."

"I took you to the pediatrician. I took you to a psychologist. I took you to a nutritionist. I took you to an Obsessive Compulsive Disorder specialist. I took you to a Cognitive Behavior specialist. I took you to a Behavioral Science specialist. I took you to a psychiatrist."

"But none of it helped. They would all tell me different versions of the same thing:

- She'll grow out of it.
- When she gets into kindergarten, she'll see the other kids around snack time and will start eating.
- When she is a teenager, her friends will start pressuring her to eat.
- When she goes to college and starts dating, she'll start trying new foods."

"Part of it was you were naturally small to begin with so I was worried about your health. You didn't sleep well and you had dark circles under your eyes. But I had dark circles too, so was it just genetic or was it because of your diet?"

"Plus the doctors were telling me she isn't getting the protein she needs. So I made sure to give you vitamins and find other ways for you to get your protein through milk and peanut butter and nuts."

"After a while when the pediatricians were setting new goals for me they just said, 'She is a selective eater and as long as she is getting the protein she needs, she'll be fine.' I began to become more accustomed to it. I didn't like it, but I accepted it as reality."

"I still felt guilty, though, and always made sure I explained to the doctors that you weren't missing any school, were rarely sick, were keeping up with your activities and seemed pretty healthy. I didn't want them to think any shortcomings I might have as a parent were unknowingly hurting my child. But it was always this question of would she be like this normally or is the picky eating affecting her health?"

"It was very confusing. It was hard on me as a mother because I just didn't understand. You get some of your drive from me and I really wanted to figure out what to do, so I would research and research and research."

"I read all kinds of books on it. I worried about it. I lost sleep on it."

"It was so troubling and worrisome to me, even more than Dad, because I was the one home with you. I was trying to be the perfect mother. I had this deep feeling of guilt and I would constantly question myself asking, 'What am I doing wrong?'"

"Through the years even my family didn't understand and would say, 'Well you're just not being tough enough with her.'"

"When you were little you were very attached to me and had stranger and separation anxiety. You would wake up at night and would want me there. You wanted me in your sight at all times from when you were a baby until you were five years old. Looking back, it was a sensitivity that your two sisters (Nelly & Mandy) didn't have, so I wondered if it had something to do with your selective eating."

"At one point one of the doctors had you take a Rorschach test to see if you had some sort of pent up hatred for Dad and me. I couldn't help being nervous and scared when you went in for that test even though I knew you loved us. It came back completely normal and showed that you loved us and had nothing but good feelings toward us."

"I didn't really think you were being picky to be stubborn or as some sort of power struggle. Instead, I thought you were just a sensitive child and by the time you went to kindergarten you'd grow out of it."

"There were times when I would just get so angry with you and would say, 'Why can't you at least try it?' Especially the watermelon. You wouldn't even try it. I would tell you, 'It just tastes like water. The worst that'll happen is you won't like it and you can just spit it out.' But you wouldn't."

"I would go back and forth between being mad that you wouldn't try anything and hurt and would say, 'Mom and Dad want this so badly for you. What you're doing, this is hurting Mom and Dad.'"

"It really began when you were about thirteen months old or maybe even earlier. You were eating creamed carrots, creamed squash and creamed peas, but as soon as we tried the Gerber creamed chicken or beef you would spit it out. Nelly and Mandy never did that. You were so young that you didn't even have a concept of being stubborn or how to manipulate us. So you had this very distinct thing at a very young age."

"The doctors would tell me to just make the same meal for everyone and put it in front of you. I was always careful to make sure I put a balanced meal of protein, starch, fruits and vegetables in front of you, hoping something would look appealing to you. But it didn't work."

"Dad and I would second guess ourselves as parents and felt like we weren't being tough enough with you."

"There was one showdown between us where I said, 'No you're going to have to eat what everyone else is eating and that's that.' You cried and cried and went for three days without eating, just sitting there watching everyone else eat. You did drink water and had a few saltine crackers, but that was it. You were so young."

"There was a point where I gave up and I said, 'I can't do this anymore.' I felt like I was hurting you. I didn't want food to be a battleground. I became numb to the comments from family and friends and didn't care anymore what the other moms said or if my family criticized me. Nobody understood."

"It wasn't fun, that's for sure, and I felt really guilty."

"Even now I still have people turn and question me and say, 'She's eating everything now? Why couldn't you do that before?'"

"I remember there was one day at a Girl Scout meeting when you were about nine or ten years old and the moms gave me such a hard time. We were all sitting around a picnic table and I pulled out your standard lunch and one of the moms said, 'Why do you let her get away with that?

Why aren't you tougher with her?' We got into quite a fight about it. I remember telling her, 'You don't know what I've been through and what I've tried with her, so mind your own business. She's happy and healthy and she's doing just fine.'"

"I was on the defense all the time. I wanted people to see that you were actually all right despite your diet."

"It was also hard having your diet be different than your little sisters', especially with you being the eldest daughter. I would say to Nelly and Mandy, 'You have to eat all your dinner,' and they would ask me, 'Why doesn't Jessie have to?' and I didn't have a good reason besides, 'You know Jessie has a different diet.' They felt that it was unfair and that the rules weren't the same for all of us."

"I think you had an aversion to how you'd imagine a new food would taste and you'd say to me, 'I don't like what it looks like. I don't like that it's squishy.' I realized there was a texture and tactile thing going on. If it didn't look right to you, there was no way you would even try it. The strawberries had little seeds on the outside so you wouldn't try them. Your senses were just way more heightened than other people. You're the only person I know who was so alert to certain textures and could immediately detect any difference."

"I remember when I changed the thread count on your sheets from 400 to 350. You came up to me and said, 'Mom, what did you do to my sheets? They aren't soft anymore.' The other girls didn't notice the change at all. I was flabbergasted!"

"There was another time I accidentally got the Welch's grape jam instead of the Welch's grape jelly and you came up to me and exclaimed, 'Why did you change the jelly on me!' I was sitting there wondering, 'What? I didn't even realize. How did you notice that?' I didn't even know I had gotten something different but you would notice any little change right away."

"Surprisingly, you loved to play with your Easy-Bake Oven and the little kitchen set we had for you. So you had no problem pretending to cook and make food for everyone, which I thought was so ironic!"

"You were such a sweet kid. I didn't even have the terrible twos with you or Nelly or Mandy. You never threw tantrums or got in trouble at school. You were so attached to us and your sisters. I would say you were normal in every way except the food selectivity. Academically, you were a star, always getting A's and outstandings in citizenship. You were a delightful child, with a good personality and open heart and you loved to learn."

"If I'm going to be honest, I didn't really have you and your sisters help out in the kitchen. I'd wake up every day and ask myself, 'Okay what am I going to do for dinner today?' Then depending on if I had all the ingredients, I'd run to the store or take something out of the freezer to thaw. I learned that the trick to being able to provide home-cooked meals each night is to always have your refrigerator stocked. I always keep stewed tomatoes and pasta in the pantry to be able to create a last-minute marinara sauce with spaghetti if I needed it. It was all I could do to get a home-cooked dinner on the table every night. Dad was working a full-time job with ten-to-twelve hour days and getting his master's degree at night. You girls were busy kids and would come home after dance lessons and do your homework and school projects and I would be cooking. The rest of my family was out of town, so it was just me, your father and you girls."

"I didn't even know how to cook in the beginning. I taught myself. I learned through trial and error, using my Betty Crocker book and lots of phone calls to my mother to ask about different dishes. In my house, my mother did the cooking and if we were hanging around the kitchen, we were in the way. So I was not in the kitchen learning how to cook from my mom while growing up. I remember calling her up after I got married though and asking, 'Mom, how do you make the pasta sauce?' I learned through observation and osmosis and experimenting on my own. Then would call her up again and ask her what to do if something didn't turn out quite right."

"I made sure that we always had a home-cooked family meal and insisted that we all sit down to eat together each night. Dad thinks this is part of why you girls are so close to each other. It made us spend that quality time together even with all of your crazy schedules with work and homework and activities. And you always wanted to be at the dinner table with us and eat at the same time even with all the unfamiliar foods. It was important to you to be there; you just didn't want to eat what the rest of the family was eating."

"I have to be honest though and say I didn't think to involve you girls in the cooking and say, 'This is what I'm making for dinner, girls. Come help me cut this up or bring me that.' We were not very involved in the kitchen with my mom when I was younger so it didn't occur to me. She did have us set the table though and once we were teenagers we helped a little bit with the cooking, but not much. No one really suggested to me that I should involve you with the food preparation for dinner while you were young."

"It felt like if I asked for your help in the kitchen, it would make you even more uncomfortable and be more complicated for me to prepare dinner. Plus, I felt like it was my job as the mom to make the meals and your job was to eat it, enjoy it, and use that extra time to get your homework done. You did want to be involved in the baking though. You didn't have a problem with that because you loved being able to eat the cakes and brownies and cookies we made."

"If there was advice I could give to parents of picky eaters it would be, 'Trust your own instincts.' When I followed the advice of: 'Don't give her anything to eat until she eats one thing you want her to,' and she refused, it was the absolute worst experience. I knew something was wrong, and I knew she wasn't a mean or spiteful child, but I just didn't know how to make it better for her."

"I would also say, 'If the advice you're getting is not working from one doctor, try another. Keep trying. Do it while they are young and see if you can break the pattern early.'"

~Judy Rohrer~

I love my mom and dad very much and I know how difficult my picky eating was for them. I'd like for the parents of picky eaters to know that IT IS NOT THEIR FAULT. So many parents of picky eaters have been pressured, insulted and judged because of their picky eaters when there really wasn't anything more they could do or anything they were doing wrong.

It is hard for professionals, and even harder for parents, to know the difference between normal fussy eating in toddlers and extreme picky eating or selective eating disorder (SED) stemming from an ingrained food phobia.

Felix Economakis describes the difference well in his article 'Top Six Myths about Selective Eating Disorder Food Phobias.'[5]

He says, "Selective Eating Disorder (SED) is not fussy eating. They are very different things. SED is a strong aversion/phobia around foods, which means even if you desperately wanted to try some appetizing looking food, you would be unable to do so, or unable to swallow it.

Fussy eating is when a person *could* eat alternative foods but they want their favorite or most exciting foods most or all of the time, or they are very fussy about food looking perfect or unblemished (e.g., a pure white chicken breast and won't eat chicken thighs or there is a dark spot on a french fry).

'Fussy eating' tends to just be a normal conservative stage during most children's development. Fussy eaters are often

---

5   Economakis, F. (2016). *Top Six Myths About Selective Eating Disorder (food phobias)*. [online] YourTango. Available at: https://www.yourtango.com/experts/felixeconomakis/top-six-myths-about-selective-eating-disorder-food-phobias [Accessed 12 Jan. 2019].

merely picky or play on the preferential treatment or special attention they get, but they are not phobic.

SED often gets overlooked and misdiagnosed by doctors and even eating disorder specialists, as they confuse the one with the other and unfortunately give very inappropriate and even harmful advice.

SED is a true phobia that just happens to be associated with foods rather than animals, objects or processes. In simple terms, due to an event or phase in the past, pain has been associated with certain foods and the system refuses to venture past its safe foods. The more this situation persists, the greater the belief that one is 'unable' to then eat new foods because of the lack of past historical successes.

A person with SED / ARFID may have health complications or be missing out on social interactions, and desperate to eat other food but their brain will make them incapable of either eating food or swallowing it. In addition, you can bribe them with—an iPad, a new car, a trip to Hawaii, $1,000 (all true bribes)—and they will still not eat a morsel of new food. This is because a phobia is present rather than a fussiness.

The American Psychiatric Association has formally recognized selective eating as an eating disorder in its diagnostic 'bible' (the DSM-IV). In its latest version (DSM-V), selective eating has been renamed Avoidant Restrictive Food Intake Disorder (ARFID). It is a real condition.

Unfortunately, without a real understanding of the dynamics of SED, most conventional approaches to therapy such as graded desensitization tend to be ineffective. What is not understood by most practitioners is the concept of 'safe food.' People with SED are highly specific about their safe foods. It does not follow that just because a person is willing to eat chicken nuggets that they can move on to trying other forms of chicken. Chicken nuggets are the safe food not 'chicken' per se. Roast chicken might as well be lettuce. The brain classifies it to all intents and purposes as if it is another food category. The same applies to potatoes. Some clients will only eat one form of potato: french fries."

French fries with salt were a safe food for me and I would not eat any other variation of a potato which meant no hash browns, no curly fries, no mashed potatoes, no baked potatoes, or any other variation of a potato.

Without a clear agreed upon definition in the medical field, for the purposes of this book I will offer the following as my definition for extremely picky eating. Extremely picky eating, also known as selective eating disorder (SED) or avoidant restrictive intake disorder (ARFID), is a form of disordered eating in children, teenagers or adults where a person's diet consists of a highly limited range of safe foods. Extremely picky eating stems from a phobia of food often developed while young which becomes stronger and more ingrained with time. An extremely picky eater may experience intense anxiety, fear, and physical symptoms when attempting to try new foods. Extremely picky eating or SED is different than conventional fussy eating during a toddler's development.

Although people do grow out of conventional fussy eating as toddlers, many people do not grow out of extreme picky eating or SED when a phobia is present and remain traumatized or stuck and unable expand their diet for years and years. Some picky eaters are able to add a few new foods to their diet like I did starting in 2012 with my food blog. However, a significant proportion have also dropped a food or two and the range of safe foods in their diet has shrunk even more. There are so many adults out there who did not "grow out it" and instead have a phobia of food and have grown up with their extreme picky eating or SED. Over time, their existing habits, beliefs, and fears around food have become more entrenched, like mine was. But with formal help and consistently implementing the right strategies, it is possible for an extremely picky eater with SED to change.

Picky Points:

- Conventional fussy eating during a toddler's development is different than extremely picky eating or Selective Eating Disorder (SED) in children, teenagers or adults.

- Children will grow out of fussy eating preferences where they could eat alternatives but want their favorite or most exciting foods.

- Children do NOT grow out of extremely picky eating or SED, which is a phobia of food usually formed early in life and reinforced with time.

- Don't blame yourself or others for your or your child's picky eating. It is not your fault. It is a phobia, not poor parenting.

- Don't give up. Keep trying. Trust your instincts.

CHAPTER 3

SAFE VS. STUBBORN

"One thing I heard from a lot of people was, 'She's just being stubborn.' But she was a baby and was just trying to take care of herself. She didn't even know how to intentionally be stubborn when she was that young." ~ Virginia Sole Smith

Virginia Sole Smith helps women with their health and nutrition. Virginia began her career giving diet advice in teen and women's magazines, and reporting on environmental health issues, including the rise of the modern alternative food movement. She spent over a decade watching that movement's obsession with whole foods and clean eating merge with the war on obesity and the belief that women's bodies, in particular, should always be smaller. But it wasn't until her own daughter stopped eating as a newborn, and Virginia was faced with making food seem safe to a traumatized child, that she realized just how many of us don't feel safe around food because our fears about body size have spun so out of control. Virginia's work has appeared in *The New York Times Magazine, Harper's, Elle* and many other publications. She's also a contributing editor with *Parents Magazine* and co-host of Comfort Food Podcast.

Virginia told me, "In 2013, my daughter came down with a rare heart condition and so breast feeding was very difficult for her. She became very ill at one year old and had to have open heart surgery. When you have a baby, the first thing you do is try to feed them. This is how babies bond and form attachments when they are born. But my daughter completely shut down after her surgery and wouldn't eat anything because her natural instinct was to protect her breathing. She would reject food and anything coming down her throat. So I had a baby recovering from surgery who wouldn't eat and was completely dependent on a feeding tube. We had to figure out how to overcome that. Being a health journalist I started researching and there wasn't a lot out of information out there at the time but I found that there are basically two camps of thought on the topic. There is 1) the behavioral therapy approach, which is a reward based approach, and 2) the child led approach, which is a positive association based approach. What I found was the first approach may be effective in the short term but not necessarily in the long term because she doesn't learn how to trust her body and instincts. She stopped eating because eating didn't feel safe, so with this approach how is she going to learn to trust herself again? How does this solve the problem of her being able to trust herself? The second approach is the child led approach, which is about creating positive associations with food. It's about making meal time a positive experience so that it's fun to be at the table with Mommy and Daddy and make a mess and play with your food. The second approach is the one we followed and now my daughter is a healthy five-year-old. She is off her feeding tube and eats completely on her own."

"We were able to tackle it before there was a lot of shame or pressure around it, which I think played a huge role in how we were able to progress so quickly. It was a logical choice for her to not feel safe around eating because she was a little baby trying to protect herself. Just taking it slowly and helping her trust herself again was key. At the time it felt like an impossible task but now I feel lucky.

"One thing I was often told was, 'Just wait for her to get hungry and she will eat.' But this didn't hold true for us. She was too deeply traumatized for that to work. If the child is not eating because they are deeply afraid of food, you can't expect for them to overcome that fear just from punishment. Which is what you are doing when you are saying you have to eat this or you won't eat anything.

"You can still create a supportive framework to try new foods and have a few comfortable options available for them to eat as well. Part of it is about treating kids and all people with respect. For example, you could say, 'Here is a little milk and banana on the table but there are these new foods on the table as well.'

"Especially for a kid when there are sensory issues involved, or they are sensitive to texture. You can't just give a kid a steak for dinner and expect for them to be able to eat it. But you're also not making a separate mac and cheese for your child for every meal either. My daughter is very comfortable with pasta now, so I'll do a pasta with different sauces and add in new or different things to the pasta, which is something she is familiar with."

Virginia's experience with helping her daughter feel safe with food again resonates with me. I've always been frustrated when people have said to me, "Oh you're just being stubborn." I didn't know how to explain to them when I was younger that, no, I wasn't just being stubborn. This was something different. I knew what it was like to be stubborn in other aspects of my life. If you wanted to play with a toy and your sister wanted to play with it as well, you could be stubborn, refusing to share the toy, but it was still possible for you. You *could* give her the toy. You just didn't *want* to. It was completely different than my picky eating when

I felt like I *could not* try a new food no matter how badly I wanted to.

As Felix Economakis says, "The assumption that a child could eat food but just holds off eating it to get some form of attention is inaccurate. I can assure you that after having heard thousands of stories from clients with SED, clients would pretty much give anything to NOT have this kind of attention.

"At school no child wants to be singled out as 'weird' or 'odd' or an object of ridicule by his or her peers. The opinion of his or her peer group means everything to a child at this age. No child wants to be left out while their peers go to camp or school trips or other activities where there are completely unfamiliar foods, yet the person with SED cannot join in and eat what everyone else is having.

"If going on a date, no young person seeks the ridicule of their prospective date. In fact, many people end up avoiding dating and develop a lot of social anxiety as they tend to feel very conscious of their eating behaviors in the presence of others.

"Not all attention is desirable.

"Moreover, there is another assumption that this is somehow a child or teenage problem. In fact, the majority of my clients have been adults who run companies, businesses, teams, households and the like. For the most part, they have taken pains to keep their behavior a secret from others (the very opposite of supposed attention seeking). Who exactly are they meant to be seeking attention from in any case? Elderly parents?

"These same adults have also been desperate enough to invest large sums of money in travel, accommodation, flights and fees to address their phobia. Not to mention I have seen a handful of clients with SED who are professional chefs (yes chefs!) and many others who have a keen interest in cooking but cannot taste their own food. They rely on others to taste it or have to go by the look, smell and feel of their cooking. No chef is going to hold themselves back in their career because of some abstract need for attention. If attention clearly does not figure in the behavior of the clients, the behavior is not happening due to attention. As with many of these myths, a little bit of deeper scrutiny reveals there is no actual evidence base for this belief."

To help compare conventional fussy eating in toddlers to extremely picky eating or selective eating disorder (SED), here is a checklist I've compiled from Dr. Kay A Toomey[6] and Alisha Grogen[7]:

Conventional Fussy Eating

- Eats twenty to twenty-five foods or more on a regular basis.
- Foods lost due to "burn out" because of a food jag are usually re-gained after a two-week break.
- Able to tolerate new foods on plate and usually can touch or taste a new food (even if reluctantly).
- Can be coaxed to occasionally try new foods.
- Will suddenly refuse a food they have preferred, but will eat it again in the future.
- Eats at least one food from most all food texture groups. Eats at least a few fruits/vegetables, carbs, and proteins.
- Sometimes eats different foods than the rest of the family.
- Bribes, rewards, and punishment will often work.
- Usually will eat foods similar to their favorites. For example, will eat a variety of chicken nuggets or pizza, they will typically not reject different brands or styles.

---

6   Toomey, K. (2010). *Picky Eaters vs. Problem Feeders | SOS Approach to Feeding*. [online] Sosapproach-conferences.com. Available at: http://sosapproach-conferences.com/resources/picky-eaters-vs-problem-feeders/ [Accessed 12 Jan. 2019].

7   Grogan, A. (2013). *Has Picky Eating Gone Too Far: Food Aversion Disorders in Kids*. [online] Your Kid's Table. Available at: https://yourkidstable.com/picky-eating-vs-problem-feeder/ [Accessed 12 Jan. 2019].

- Sometimes reported by parent as a "picky eater" at wellness check-ups.

Extremely Picky Eater with Selective Eating Disorder

- Eats usually less than twenty different foods consistently, maybe as few as one to three.
- Foods lost due to food jags are NOT re-acquired.
- Cries, "falls apart" or becomes emotionally upset when presented with new foods.
- May gag, shudder, or vomit at the site or taste of new foods.
- Common picky eating strategies like the "try a bite" rule and punishment often don't help.
- Refuses entire categories of food groups or textures (vegetables, meat, etc.).
- Seems to have sensory issues with the food (the way it smells, looks, feels, etc.).
- Almost always eats different foods than the rest of the family.
- Will suddenly refuse a food they previously preferred and never eat it again.
- May insist on foods being prepared in specific ways or will only eat a specific brand/style of food.
- Persistently reported by parent as a "picky eater" across multiple wellness check-ups.

Picky Points:

- Children and adults with SED often don't feel safe with food.
- Children and adults with SED are not just "being stubborn."
- Most people don't want the kind of attention picky eating creates.
- A positive association approach to new food helps an extremely picky eater feel safe around food and trust his or her body.

CHAPTER 4

FOOD CONSCIOUS

—

Imagine feeling a sense of intense anxiety or uncontrollable dread every time a new food is put in front of you. Simply the thought of tasting it makes you start to sweat and feel as though you'll gag or retch, regardless of how much you try to reassure yourself that you will be okay.

You try to taste certain food with the hope that willpower alone will prevail. You're ready. You sit down with a new food. And yet, you still cannot bring yourself to eat it—no matter how much you want to.

After Felix's treatment I became very curious about how in the world his therapy worked for me. It was hard to believe— after so many years of picky eating and seeing doctor after doctor after doctor without any of them helping—that in just a few hours I no longer had the anxiety and fear around trying new foods I'd lived with my entire life. I mean really, how is that possible?

I talked with Felix and then started reading and researching everything I could get my hands on that had to do with food and psychology and implementing change. I researched... and researched...and researched some more.

Extremely picky eating or SED in adults and teenagers at its core is a phobia. A phobia is an extreme or irrational fear or aversion to something. Picky eating is an intense fear of trying new food. Something happened while the picky eater was young, which created a subconscious fear of food.

In "When Children Won't Eat: Understanding the 'Why's' and How to Help" by Kay A. Toomey PHD, she explains:

"Learning about food happens in two ways:

1. When a connection is made in time between one natural event, behavior or object and another neutral stimulus.
    a. *Example: Aversion to a type of alcohol after drinking too much of it one time.*
2. Through reinforcement and punishment.

If you learn at a young age that food = scary, your subconscious mind does what it can to protect you from food. That is where the limited safe foods come from for a picky eater. They are rules that your subconscious creates to try and keep you safe. Your subconscious mind is essentially saying, "Okay I know these foods are safe and won't hurt me so I should stick to those and nothing else."[8]

For extremely picky eaters, due to an event or phase in the past, pain or fear has been associated with new foods and the system refuses to venture past its safe foods. The more this situation persists, the greater the belief one is 'unable' to then eat new foods because of the lack of historic success. This is very different than conventional fussy eating in toddlers, which does not involve a phobia, so picky eating and SED often get overlooked and misdiagnosed by doctors and therapists, as they confuse one with the other.

According to anxiety.org, "Phobias involve intense fear surrounding an object or situation that realistically poses little or no real danger. They are different from common fears in that the associated anxiety is so strong it interferes with daily life and the ability to function normally. People suffering from phobias may go to extreme lengths to avoid encountering or experiencing the feared object or

8   Toomey, K. (2010). *When Children Won't Eat: Understanding the "Why's" and How to Help.*

situation. Though many people with phobias realize their worry is unrealistic or unwarranted, feelings of fear and anxiety persist and seem unmanageable, leaving sufferers feeling out of control."[9]

This makes complete sense to me and aligns with how I felt about my picky eating. This perfectly describes what it was like any time I would attempt to try something new. I could not logically make sense of why I couldn't "just eat it." I could see all my friends and family eating these foods around me with nothing bad happening, yet every time anyone would even put a new food on my plate, I would start sweating, become anxious and uncomfortable, and freak out.

The American Psychiatric Association identifies three types of phobias:

- Specific Phobia: Going to extreme lengths to avoid an activity or object because of fear of danger or harm.
  - *Examples: Fear of heights, snakes, spiders*
- Social Phobia: A fear of being humiliated or underperforming in social situations, also known as social anxiety disorder.
  - *Examples: Fear of public speaking, public restrooms, eating in front of others*

---

9   Anxiety.org. (2019). *Phobias.* [online] Available at: https://www.anxiety.org/phobias [Accessed 12 Jan. 2019].

- Agoraphobia: Feeling discomfort in situations where escape is difficult or help is not readily available.
  - *Examples: Fear of leaving the house, public transportation, small spaces*

Picky eating falls under the specific phobia category. Picky eaters will go to extreme lengths to avoid trying new foods because of their fear of food. Think of it the same way you would as someone with a phobia of spiders. What if every time someone put a new food on your plate it felt as though they were putting an open jar of spiders in front of you and asking you to stick your hand in even though you are severely afraid of them? For picky eaters, our "spider" is food and we are confronted with it every single day, three times a day, seven days a week, fifty-two weeks a year and almost always with lots of other people around.

Symptoms of phobias are similar to those of a panic attack. When faced with the specific object, activity, or situation that is the subject of intense fear, an individual with a phobia may exhibit the following symptoms:

- Uncontrollable feelings of anxiety, dread, and panic
- Rapid heart rate
- Difficulty breathing
- Sweating
- Trembling, shaking

- Abdominal discomfort
- Tightening of the chest and feelings of choking
- Nausea and dizziness
- Hot or cold flashes
- An overwhelming desire to escape

Most phobias develop in childhood, and are commonly passed down by a family member. However, the main cause of phobias is still unknown. Frequent causes of phobias include:

- Traumatic experience involving object of fear
- Experiencing a panic attack in a specific situation or around an object
- Witnessing someone else being harmed by a specific activity or object
- Hearing a tragic story involving a specific activity or object

Phobias are treatable, and the treatments are usually very effective. Thankfully, this includes food phobias for extremely picky eaters with SED.

Picky Points:

- Extremely picky eating or SED is a specific phobia of food.
- A picky eating food phobia usually develops during childhood.

- Extremely picky eaters with SED experience intense anxiety when attempting to try new foods.
- Safe foods and a limited diet is the subconscious mind's way of trying to keep an extremely picky eater safe.
- Similar to other phobias, a food phobia can be treated.

RECIPE

CRISPY HOME FRIES

Our first recipe is for extra crispy home fries. This is my favorite french fry alternative that you can easily make right at home. The shape is slightly different than a french fry but the texture is very similar. They are very crisp and crunchy on the outside and soft of the inside. An added bonus with these home fries is they are better for you than french fries. You don't have all that oil because you are roasting them instead of deep frying them but they are still nice and crispy, salty and tasty!

INGREDIENTS

- 1 Russet Potato
- 1 Tbsp Olive Oil
- Salt

- Pepper
- Garlic Powder

INSTRUCTIONS

1. Heat oven at 450°F. Put an aluminum foil covered pan in the oven as it heats up.

2. Peel potato, cut into small pieces.

3. Boil potatoes for 5–10 minutes until it is just about cooked through when you poke it with a fork and it starts to give.

4. Drain and dry the potatoes.

5. Dry them again. You want them as dry as possible.

6. Put them in a bowl. Add olive oil, salt, pepper and garlic powder and mix together coating potatoes.

7. Take the pan out of the oven. Spread the potatoes out on the aluminum covered pan with lots of space so they aren't touching.

8. Pop in the oven and roast for 10–15 minutes on one side.

9. Take them out and turn them.

10. Roast for another 10–15 minutes on another side.

11. Take them out when they've turned light brown and crispy. Enjoy!

PART 2

EXPOSURE AND INVOLVEMENT

This section is about some of the very first steps to take if you are an extremely picky eater. We dive into how exposure to new foods and involvement in the kitchen can help picky eaters (or anyone) try new foods and expand their diet regardless of age. We learn how having fun, playing with our food, and involving all of our senses can make a big difference. We even take a look at a scientifically backed approach extremely picky eaters can start using right away to decrease their phobia of food.

CHAPTER 5

EXPOSURE HELPS

———

"If you tell them to eat a piece of kale they'll spit it in your face, but if you ask them to make a kale salad, they might actually try it. It's a completely different ask with often a completely different result." ~Emily Sauerman

Emily Capo Sauerman founded a nonprofit called Taste Quest in 2018 which provides a kid's food magazine and application designed to help kids learn about food and cooking through interactive play. The content is full of games and challenges all geared to help kids learn about food through play. As they play, they log points in the app, which gets sponsored by local businesses who donate to local food-focused charities. Her mission is to create a vehicle for kids to learn about food, have a ton of fun, pay it forward and create a better, healthier, well-rounded relationship with food.

Emily says, "You can't get someone to change their habits just by telling them what to do, but when these kids actually make the food themselves, they're way more likely to actually eat it. The reason why is because it's interactive; it's an activity; it's a game! It's that idea that when you are playing a game you are not under threat, and you are not trying to reach goals that are out of your reach. You think more optimistically, more confidently and that's what we want to build in kids in general. I think food is a great vehicle for doing that."

As Emily works with kids through her magazine, her mantra is simple, "Cooking is a superpower." She has seen its transformative work in her own family. Her cousin's son, Mason, who was at the time about eight years old, was diagnosed with hyperactivity and ADHD and was normally bouncing off the walls. His parents were struggling daily with his tantrums and high energy when they all came to visit and stayed at Emily's house for a few days. She thought, "Since I love to cook, maybe cooking could be a really good activity for the kids."

So she decided to make crepes for breakfast and invited Mason and his brother, Ethan, to participate. For crepes once you've got the batter made; it's really just about waiting as you cook one crepe at a time in the pan. So she told Mason, "Go ahead and get up on the step stool and butter the pan for me in between each crepe." Not only did he do it but he stood there armed with his silicone brush for the whole forty-five minutes while they cooked!

Later that night they decided to make homemade pizzas. Emily set aside some of the toppings that she thought just the grownups would want to have. Mason didn't realize that, however, and was full of so much curiosity about all of the ingredients and wanted to be involved in every step of the process. For every ingredient he would ask what it was and then add it to his pizza.

"What's that?" "Asparagus." "Give it to me."

"What's that?" "Goat Cheese." "Give it to me."

"What's that?" "Pepperoni." "Give it to me."

Emily was thrilled, "He put every single topping we had on his pizza. He created a pizza that you would normally pay $15 to eat in a restaurant and it was amazing. He ate the whole thing!"

As Emily says, "There is something to be said about the novelty of cooking, especially for kids. There is also something to be said about the 'do it yourself' factor that takes creativity, concentration, and commitment, and that really panned out in Mason's case. Not only did he really enjoy making the food but he also ate it all!"

She said, "My eighteen-month-old wants to help out in the kitchen and she wants to do things correctly. She wants to use the big spoon, touch things, and be involved. It's about giving the kids a real job. Doing something real is a huge motivator. They're cooking with real food, not a playdough cooking station. They're actually making a meal for their family. Kids like to see that they helped make what they're eating and what their family is eating."

Emily says, "Make it a game. It's productive. It's fun. The goal is to introduce your child to different kinds of eating and to what is delicious. We can show them that not all healthy food tastes bad but rather can taste really good, that food from other cultures isn't scary but just has different flavors, and that fresh food from your local farmer may not be symetrical but is delicious."

Emily continued, "As a person who has always loved food, I think cooking is really fun and it's really rewarding. There are ways to make it affordable and ways to make it quick. I do it not only because it's fun but also because I know it's good for me and my family."

Just simple exposure to new foods while helping out in the kitchen was enough for Mason to want to try these new foods. That isn't always the case right away for every child but repeated exposure to new foods in ways like this where the child is touching the food, washing it, cutting it up, and is actively involved in the preparation of the food will make a child more likely to try it in the long run.

This exposure to new foods and involvement in the kitchen is great for all children but it is especially important to do with extremely picky eaters or children with SED. If a fear around food was formed while they were younger, the gradual exposure to new foods in comfortable settings will help start to ease this fear and make new food seem more familiar and safe. You don't want food and eating to be a chore or scary. It isn't school and it shouldn't feel like work. It usually isn't dangerous. It should be enjoyable and fun!

What you are essentially doing by exposing you extremely picky eater to different foods in a nonthreatening way is introducing extinction learning to your child. Extinction learning refers to the gradual decrease in response to a conditioned stimulus that occurs when the stimulus is presented without reinforcement. The term "extinction" was first used by Ivan Pavlov in reference to his observation that the conditioned response to a cue that predicted food delivery decreased and eventually disappeared when food no longer followed the cue. In Pavlovian fear conditioning, a previously neutral stimulus comes to elicit a fear response through pairing with an aversive reinforcer, such as an electric shock or a loud noise. During extinction learning, a new association with the stimulus is learned that inhibits the expression of the original fear memory. Extinction learning serves as the foundation of exposure therapy, which is commonly used to treat pathological fears.

When you are involving your children in the cooking process, you are essentially showing them that food isn't as scary as they currently believe. The more they are exposed to new foods and see that these new foods are not reinforcing their fear of it but instead are creating a new positive association (fun, interesting) the more they will be more likely to try something new.

Expose kids to new foods in a variety of different ways. Keep it fun and playful for everyone. Start small and get creative. This could be anything from prepping food to measuring flour in the kitchen. Here are some ideas to get you started:

- Find new foods in the kitchen.
- Watch cooking TV shows.
- Pick up new foods at the grocery store.
- Smell different foods at the farmers market

- Play with your food.
- Prep the food in the kitchen.
- Plant a garden.
- Buy something you've never used before and figure out what to do with it.
- Try to reproduce something you had at a restaurant.

Picky Points:

- Children are more likely to try something new if they are involved in preparing it.
- Exposure therapy uses extinction learning to treat pathological fears.
- Expose your child to different kinds of eating, different kinds of cooking, different flavors, different textures, and different ingredients.
- Involve kids in the kitchen with real tasks.
- Make cooking and eating fun and playful to create positive associations with food.

CHAPTER 6

INVOLVE THEM EARLY ON!

———

"Food becomes a big part of your lifestyle and the stories that you develop throughout your life. People have different jobs, crafts and hobbies but everybody eats. Everyone has food experiences and memories with food." ~Dad

I come from a family of really great cooks.

Although I was an extremely picky eater, Mom, Dad, Grandma Ann, Grandma Jean, and my sisters, Janelle (Nelly) and Amanda (Mandy), all love and appreciate good food and know their way around a kitchen. My mom is known for her Italian cooking, my Dad for his French and German cooking and my sisters for trying new healthy recipes.

It all started for my dad at a very young age as the youngest of four children when he would help my grandma out in the kitchen.

When he was about seven years old, he'd say to my grandma, "You know, I really want crepes for breakfast." Grandma would turn to him and say, "Okay if you want that for your meal, then go ahead and make the batter for it and I'll cook it up with you." She would really involve him in the process in the kitchen and then she would cook it for him when he wasn't old enough yet to do the cooking. That was their little agreement. If he ever wanted something special, she would let him do it if he helped with the preparation and did some of the work.

Every year during the fall in October or November, Grandma and Grandpa would buy half a side of beef from Uncle Bud who owned a slaughterhouse in Buffalo, New York. It was a really good way to get good meat for a good price. The slaughterhouse would drop it off at their house and then Grandma would need to break it all down into each set of steaks, package it, tape it up, mark it and freeze it. The process would take all day, but they would inevitably get it done the day it was dropped off because they didn't have a place to store that much meat besides the freezer. They couldn't leave the meat out and there wasn't enough space in the refrigerator. Usually they had it all nicely planned for the meat to arrive on a Saturday or a Sunday so everyone was home and able to help.

One year, when my dad was ten years old, the box showed up during the week while all the kids were in school. So my grandma walked over to the elementary school and went in to talk with the school administrator. She said, "I need my son today." She was told, "What do you mean? He's in class; you can't take him out of class." And she said, "Oh yes I can. I need my son's help today and I'm taking him home with me!" And she did. She knew my dad was such a good helper. So she brought him home from school to help with breaking down and freezing all the meat for that year.

I'm sure what he would have learned in class that day was valuable, but I doubt he would still remember that lesson from class. And yet, he remembers the day he went home to help his mom and was taught a valuable lesson in the process—not only about food preparation but also about family responsibility and helping when needed.

The first time my dad really started learning how to cook came from his desire for hamburgers. He had a phase when he was twelve years old where he would proclaim to my grandma, "I want a hamburger!" at every single meal for months in a row.

Finally, Grandma said to herself, "Well enough of that," and she made a bunch of hamburger patties and put them in the freezer. Then she told my dad, "Okay, if you want a hamburger, you've got to grab a patty out of the freezer, put it in the pan and fry it up."

She showed him how to cook the hamburger in the frying pan the first time and then it was up to him to take on the responsibility to cook it after that. And he did. He would grab his hamburger patties and make these tiny little hamburgers, add some celery salt and put them on sliced bread with a little bit of ketchup and mustard. He would sit there and have his hamburgers for whatever meal he wanted. That was the first time he truly learned how to cook. It was from his desire of really, really wanting to eat hamburgers!

Looking back on these experiences my dad commented, "The whole experience defines quality time. Food was simply the mechanism but the experiences we shared counted more. It didn't matter whether it was crepes, packing meat, or cooking hamburgers; the experiences were the valuable part.

"Feeding someone is one thing but cooking with someone is something different. It requires you to spend extra time together. Even though I was learning to cook, I didn't know it at the time. I was just trying to eat a hamburger, something I wanted, or tolerating my mom or dad's whim. But that quality time we spent cooking or working together created memorable experiences that I'll never forget."

When he left for college, Grandma made him a set of fifteen to twenty regular white index cards with some simple reliable recipes for him that he could actually cook himself. That was one of the things she handed him when he was going off to college and said, "Here, you need to be able to cook." They were recipes for things like spaghetti sauce, sloppy joes, grilled cheese, and chili. That was the next step in his learning process. He no longer had someone looking over his shoulder but had to learn to do it for himself. In college you study for your desired profession, but you also learn how to be independent, how to do your laundry, how to manage your time and how to cook and feed yourself. It's an important time of transition and when a lot of your food habits and behaviors become established.

While in college, as my dad came across new recipes he wanted to learn how to cook, he would call Grandma up and ask, "How do I do it?" One of the times that he called Grandma was when he wanted to make a roast chicken.

He said, "I wanted to impress this girl (your mother) so I had to call up Grandma and ask her how to cook a roast chicken for our date. I got this big roast chicken and thinking back on it now it didn't really turn out that great because we were just learning. We didn't know how to roast it right and it was much bigger than we thought, so we undercooked it, didn't spice it quite right and didn't know how to slice it. But it didn't really matter because when you're learning and cooking for someone you care about, it doesn't have to be perfect. It's really a way to show love."

He continued, "Years later, that became a dish that Mom and I wanted to learn how to cook better. We graduated college and were engaged to be married, and we went out and bought the frugal gourmet cook book to try it again. That was our very first cook book. We took Grandma's recipe and mixed it with the frugal gourmet recipe and put our own twist on it. Now it's become a family recipe. We take a chicken and stuff it with chopped onions and then roast it. Then we take the onions and the drippings and make that into a simple sauce. Then we serve the roast chicken and sauce over pasta with some Parmesan cheese. All starting from that little experiment in college when I was trying to impress Mom for a date and now it has turned into one of our favorite family recipes that we still make."

"Food was simply a necessity in those college and young professional years. But my philosophy has changed about food. Now I see it as something pleasurable to do," said my dad.

Some of our other family favorites that my dad cooks are his German potato pancakes and his delicious duck confit with orange sauce. For the duck confit he takes a whole duck, breaks it down (which is quite a process!) and then boils the duck fat to use for cooking the duck meat while creating a sweet and savory orange grand marinier sauce to pair with it. Delicious!

Involving children in the kitchen is not only very important for extremely picky eaters but really important for all children growing up and could benefit them for years to come. It is about helping kids love food, encouraging their natural curiosity, and establishing good eating habits. There are so many benefits to children helping out in the kitchen, and if your child is a picky eater, it is an important step.

But why sit a 3-year-old at the cutting board when you're busy and they're occupied? Plenty of parents are reluctant to encourage a toddler to abandon that episode of "Dora the Explorer" in favor of stirring a pot. By dinnertime, mom or dad is often tired and out of patience. Some kinds of "help" don't get food on the table. Children spill, they switch the mixer to high when your back is turned, and they're not safe around stoves and knives. Letting them do most things takes vastly longer than just doing them yourself. As for older children, maybe they're "just not interested." Sports, homework, pressing social obligations ... they're busy, after all. They barely have time to get to the table, let alone put food on it. But that early involvement in the kitchen pays off for both young and older children. Start small and choose one meal a week for your children to be kitchen helpers.

Here are five reasons you should involve young and old children in the kitchen:

- Children who cook are children who taste, and sometimes try new foods.
- Children who cook say "I can," not "I can't." It builds self-esteem and confidence that a child can take well beyond the kitchen.
- Cooking fosters a habit that will have lifelong health benefits. The single most important thing you can do for your health is to cook at home.
- Children who cook gain real-life math, science, comprehension and communication skills.
- Cooking brings cooks of all ages closer. For better or worse, you will get to know your children, and they you, more deeply when you cook with them.

Make your kitchen kid-friendly and stock items your child can use. Set aside safe tools (mixing bowls, spatulas, spoons, etc.) and let him or her pick which one to use. Assign age-appropriate tasks.

- Measuring or mixing ingredients
- Greasing a pan
- Tossing together salad ingredients.
- Even a very young child can get involved by selecting cupcake liners or shaking sprinkles onto a cookie.

Extremely picky eaters may be hesitant at first and not want to get their hands dirty with new, wet or unfamiliar foods, but that's okay. If that is the case, start with them helping in the kitchen with nonfood products, by picking up measuring spoons, grabbing a pan, pulling the vegetables out of the fridge while they are still in their plastic bag or just bringing you a dry potato. Any level of involvement in the kitchen will help extremely picky eaters with SED over time. Before you know it they will start getting their hands dirty too and maybe even start trying some of the new foods you are cooking with.

Picky Points:

- Kids love to help out and can do more than you would think!
- Have kids help cook something THEY choose and want to eat.
- There are long-lasting benefits for children and extremely picky eaters who are involved in the kitchen.
- Start small. Choose one meal a week where your child can be a kitchen helper.

CHAPTER 7

PLAY WITH YOUR FOOD

———

"Children can sometimes feel unsafe or pressured with food and can develop a negative association with food. The overarching goal is to make that person or child feel safe and in control again while challenging them at a level where they can feel successful." ~Jennifer Peterson

Meet Jen.

Jennifer Peterson has worked at many level 1 children's hospitals in San Diego, California. Hospitals and trauma centers vary in their specific capabilities and are identified by level designations with level 1 being the highest in capabilities. She is a pediatric speech pathologist who specializes in working with problem eaters, infant feeding, cleft palates, brain injuries, autism, apraxia, and Down syndrome. The children's hospital where Jen works takes a cognitive approach to help children learn about different foods by creating a group where the kids are food explorers or food scientists. It is like a science class where they take out the stress of eating it and instead are just exploring food and learning about it. Every week Jen explores a new food and will ask the kids, "Do you want to try it?" and understands when most of the time the answer is "Nope!" After ten to twenty sessions, usually the kids start to become curious about it.

Jen said, "Sometimes it only takes one session, sometimes twenty, and sometimes a hundred. Every kid is different. Although kids usually tolerate it after one to two sessions once they learn they don't have to eat it. Some kids will just eat it on day two or three when they learn they are in control."

On one particular day Jen was working with this adorable ten-year-old kid who has Asperger's and they were going to explore and learn about tomatoes. This little boy hated the color red and these tomatoes were definitely red! He made sure to remind her of that fact as soon as they met, telling her again, "I don't eat red!" She said, "Okay that's fine. I don't eat purple but we are going to learn about tomatoes today. You don't have to eat it if you don't want to."

So they took the tomato and cut it up and squished it around in their fingers and saw that it was really slimy, and he was fascinated. All of a sudden he exclaimed, "Oh wow, look at that!" as he squeezed the tomato and watched the juice from it fall onto the table.

Jen jumped in and said, "Wow, look, the juice is clear, what do you think about trying that?" He looked at her and just said, "I'm not crazy." But then he noticed that the seeds in the tomato were yellow and asked, "Can you eat that?" and Jen said, "Yeah, I think you can! Those seeds are yellow and you've had bananas, which are yellow, so what do you think?"

He paused and looked at her and said, "Yeah, okay," and popped the seeds into his mouth! Sometimes all you have to do to help someone is just meet them where they're at.

Jen was able to make this tomato fun to play with and much more approachable to this ten-year-old once he saw the yellow seeds inside. She was able to link the yellow seeds to other yellow foods he had tried. A simple change in the way you think about something or perceive it can make a huge difference when you are being exposed to new foods.

In addition, Jen said, "Having the child involved in prepping and preparing the food even when they are really young is important. Just opening the applesauce can be overwhelming for a two-year-old, but drumsticks with carrots is easy for young kids and can be fun."

As Ruth Reichl, a prominent restaurant reviewer says, "Eating is a learned behavior. There's a reason why Japanese children get up in the morning and eat fish and rice and seaweed, and American children get up in the morning and eat Pop-Tarts. That's what we've trained them to do. It is our job to train the next generation to eat in ways that are healthy for them."[10]

There is a myth in the food world. Many people believe that eating is completely instinctual and that no matter what happens, a child will eat. But this is not true. We are born with hunger cues and have the instinct to satisfy our hunger, but how we eat, what we eat, how much we eat and where we eat is all learned. With the majority of our eating behaviors learned, it is possible to teach yourself or someone else new eating behaviors.

Take one new food and sit down with your child and play around with it. Cut the food into unusual shapes. Turn your broccoli into trees, cauliflowers into clouds, or yellow squash into a sun. Only explore one new food at a time so you don't overwhelm your picky eater. Think of it as an experiment and

10 Christians, L. (2015). *Eating is a learned behavior. Ruth Reichl talks food criticism, 'kids food' and what we throw away.* [online] Madison. com. Available at: https://madison.com/ct/entertainment/dining/eating-is-a-learned-behavior-ruth-reichl-talks-food-criticism/article_6e78e9db-3cfe-51d6-b92c-31944d09c853.html [Accessed 12 Jan. 2019].

that you are both food scientists trying to discover everything you can about this new food. You might even have some fun too rediscovering and learning about the food you eat.

For example: Grab a strawberry and spend five minutes or more to really look at it with a fresh perspective.

- What color are all those little seeds on the outside?
- Do you see the little tiny hairs that are there as well?
- How does it change color from green with the leaves at the top down to different shades of red towards the tip?
- What does it smell like?
- When you cut into it, how hard, soft or squishy is it?
- What are those little crystallized sugars on the inside?
- Does the smell increase or decrease when you cut into it?
- How dry, wet or juicy is it?

Bring a fun new sense of curiosity and see how much you can learn about a strawberry with your child. It might even give you a whole new appreciation for strawberries!

Picky Points:

- Play with your food and have fun!
- Experiment and create a food scientist culture where you focus on details and analyze the new foods taste/texture/color/shape/ etc.

- Only present one new food at a time to an extremely picky eater.
- Introduce learning foods at dinner that you all learn about but are not required to try.

CHAPTER 8

SEE, SMELL AND TOUCH FIRST

———

"If there is a new food you or your child hasn't tried before, instead of trying to taste it right away, try getting used to it with your other senses first." ~ Jessica Rohrer

When I was younger, even touching a new food was a rare occurrence for me. If I didn't like the way something looked, I would not even tolerate it on my plate. When my mom tried putting new foods on my plate I would push the whole plate away and would not want to eat anything that had been on the plate (even if it was a PB&J). I would say, "Mom, it touched the other food; I can't eat it!" I had such a strong aversion to touching or even smelling all but a few chosen foods. Of all the household chores, I would avoid washing the dishes like the plague because you would have to touch all this gross leftover food. Slimy, sticky, gross.

For years and years this is how it remained. My parents and family and friends and therapists would try to get me to just try one bite of something new but didn't realize I had such a deep phobia I wasn't even comfortable with touching these foods or having them near me, much less actually taking a bite of them. There were so many steps in between that we needed to cover before I would be anywhere close to comfortable enough with a new food to try a bite of it.

However, over the course of years I was unconsciously using something called the SOS approach. I didn't realize that is what it was at the time.

Developed by Dr. Kay A. Toomey, a pediatric psychologist who has worked for nearly thirty years with children who don't eat, the SOS (Sequential Oral Sensory) Approach to Feeding is an effective program to address problematic feeding behaviors in a variety of settings and populations. In addition to being a Clinical Consultant for the Feeding Clinic at STAR Institute, Dr. Toomey speaks nationally and internationally about her approach. She also acts as a consultant to Gerber Products. Dr. Toomey helped establish The Children's Hospital Pediatric Oral Feeding Clinic in Denver and Rose Medical Center's Pediatric Feeding Center, also in

Denver. Dr. Toomey co-chaired the Pediatric Therapy Services Department at Rose Medical Center prior to entering private practice.

Her highly effective, family-centered SOS approach to feeding has been successful and is used worldwide to assess and treat infants, children and adolescents with feeding problems. The SOS approach uses an interdisciplinary team approach, which assesses the "whole child": organ systems, muscles, development, sensory processing, oral-motor skills, learning, behavior and cognition, nutrition and the environment.

The SOS approach focuses on increasing a child's comfort level by exploring and learning about the different properties of food. The program allows a child to interact with food in a playful, non-stressful way, beginning with the ability to tolerate the food in the room and in front of him or her—then moving on to touching, kissing, and eventually tasting and eating foods.

I'd never heard of this before and had no idea what the SOS approach was, but looking back now, I can see that I was using this approach on my own for years and years leading up to when I met Felix Economakis. As simple as it sounds, starting to watch Top Chef was one of the first visual steps that helped along the way. I know it is just a TV show, but it was a way for me to learn about new foods in a very safe setting where there was no pressure to try anything. I could learn about food and see some incredibly passionate people work with food at a distance. It sparked my curiosity without the pressure to eat anything.

"I think of food TV this way—all the fun and none of the calories," said Gail Simmons from Top Chef. Top Chef is still one of my favorite shows and my curiosity has continued to grow with shows like Chef's Table, MasterChef and Ugly Delicious.

Under the *SOS* approach this would fall under the visual category in the hierarchy. Some studies even suggest that making toddlers familiar with new foods—by presenting them with images in picture books—has a positive effect on food acceptance.[11]

One of the foods I absolutely would not try was chicken. I struggled with the thought of even handling chicken. It wasn't until 2014 that started to change when my dog, Madison, was really sick with Irritable Bowel Syndrome (IBS). She was a beautiful red and white Siberian husky with blue eyes and lots of spirit. With her IBS, though, she would get sick

---

11 Dewar, G. (2009). *The science of picky eaters: Why do children reject foods that we find tasty?*. [online] Parentingscience.com. Available at: https://www.parentingscience.com/picky-eaters.html [Accessed 12 Jan. 2019].

and then wouldn't want to eat anything. To try and get her to eat something after not feeling well, I needed to give her a bland diet that her stomach could tolerate. The vet recommended rice and chicken and I thought, "Oh no." I didn't eat either of those foods at the time and was very uncomfortable with both. But I loved Madison and was so concerned for her when she wasn't eating. So I started preparing the chicken and rice while touching it as little as possible. But when she still wouldn't eat anything I eventually grabbed a little bit of rice in my hand to try to get her to eat it from my hand, which occasionally worked.

I still didn't eat either chicken or rice, but I slowly started to become accustomed to them as I was preparing them for Madison. I knew I still didn't have to eat them but I was touching them. Madison couldn't eat any of the normal packaged dog treats so when I was training her I had to use the plain chicken as her dog treats.

I was extremely uncomfortable with it. It was so slimy and wet especially as my dog was trying to lick it out of my hand. I didn't like it, but after touching it over and over again, eventually I got used to it and could do it. I still wasn't eating chicken or rice but it was a step in the right direction for me and an important step along the way. I could touch them and prepare them, which was more than I could ever say about those two foods before.

I wish I had realized earlier how much of a difference getting accustomed to touching new foods and being involved in the cooking process could make. For me it felt very black and white. Either I had to try this huge new scary food all at once or there was nothing I could do without any options in between. But you can make progress towards trying new foods by involving your other senses first. Start getting used to new foods visually. Learn about them. Try touching and smelling them first.

Over the course of many years I slowly moved myself through the steps in the exposure hierarchy, and eventually, I started trying one small bite of different foods on my own. I started with foods that were similar in some way to the foods I already ate like a different type of ice cream. By 2012 I was writing about my attempts and slow progress with trying new foods in my picky eater blog until I finally had my therapy session with Felix.

Here is a brief guide on how to move through the SOS approach and exposure hierarchy. Since this is a sensory-based approach, an extremely picky eater will get used to a new food through the use of their senses: sight, touch, smell, and taste.

- Start with visual acceptance of new foods by having a new food in the room or on the table but not in the picky eater's personal space. Talk about it, be curious about it, learn about it but make sure there is no pressure to try it. Then work toward the picky eater tolerating it within his or her personal space up to a point where they are willing to put it on their plate or pass it to someone else.

- Next work on their sense of touch and come up with different ways for them to touch new foods, such as having your picky eater pick up the new food at the grocery store or at the farmers market. Have your picky eater touch the new food with a utensil at the dinner table or grab it from the pantry or fridge for you, even if it is in a bag or container.
- Next work on their sense of smell. Ask them questions to think about what they are smelling. They could describe what it smells like or you could ask if it smells similar to anything else they've had before. You can see if they will bring it closer to their face to smell it. Does it smell interesting or good? This was always such an interesting thing to me because there are some foods that I would smell, and thought they smelled good—yet still wouldn't eat. For example pizza. I thought pizza smelled great with the bread and cheese cooking in the oven but I could not eat a pepperoni pizza with red sauce no matter how good I thought it smelled. It was still intriguing, though. There are also several foods that I do not think smell appetizing even if they taste okay such as seafood like tuna; this simply does not smell appetizing to me. I've even been surprised by some foods that do not actually taste like what I thought they would based on their smell.

- After you've achieved acceptance through sight, touch and smell, you can start to work toward taste and one small bite of the food through food chaining. Food chaining is where you try something similar in taste or texture to something already known or familiar to you. You can have the picky eater just bring the food closer to their mouth with different games where they bring it to their lips, kiss it, lick it, or take a small bite that they spit out, chew, or eventually swallow.

For more information about *SOS* Approach and Exposure Hierarchy, visit the Toomey & Associates – *SOS* Approach to Feeding website.[12]

Picky Points:

- There are several steps to take before asking a picky eater to try a bite of a new food.
- Try the *SOS* approach when trying new foods, starting with the sense of sight, moving through touch and smell until you reach the sense of taste.
- Visual—get comfortable seeing it and having it in your presence
- Tactile—touch it
- Olfactory—smell it

12 Sosapproach-conferences.com. (2017). *The SOS Approach | SOS Approach to Feeding*. [online] Available at: http://sosapproach-conferences.com/about-us/the-sos-approach/ [Accessed 12 Jan. 2019].

- Taste—lick it, take a small bite, chew it, swallow it
- Use food chaining. Start with foods that are similar in taste or texture to something the extremely picky eater is already comfortable with.

CHAPTER 9

REPEAT, REPEAT, REPEAT

———

"One thing I encourage parents to do is to get their kids involved in meal prep. That way your kid is touching it, chopping it, peeling it, and smelling it." ~Sarah Keene

Sarah Keene and her husband Kyle are the cofounders of Project Play Therapy in Nashville, Tennessee. Sarah is a licensed and registered Occupational Therapist with a strong passion to provide evidence and results-driven therapy that is client-centered and advocates for the community. Her background is in both private practice and school-based Occupational Therapy, with an emphasis in sensory integration, fine/gross motor intervention and environmental modifications to aid in learning. Along with picky eaters, she also serves children who display difficulty in handwriting, problem solving, transitions and attention, children with autism spectrum disorder, sensory processing disorder, and Down syndrome or cerebral palsy diagnosis. Project Play Therapy prides itself on offering services consisting of evidence-based and results-driven therapy while always remaining client-centered.

Sarah said, "While working in the US, Europe and Asia, my husband and I observed an overall lack of knowledge, services and advocacy for pediatric Occupational Therapy."

"As such, we have dedicated ourselves to launching Project Play Therapy to promote functional independence across all environments (school, community, home) through the use of a child's primary occupation: PLAY! As founders, Kyle and I have combined our skillsets to first improve therapy for the population with special needs locally, and second, work toward our dream of making a difference globally."

Sarah uses the Sequential Oral Sensory (SOS) approach, which works fantastically for extremely picky eaters with SED—especially while they are young before their phobia is too deeply ingrained.

As discussed earlier, you really move through a hierarchy of the senses. It starts with your visual sense and being comfortable with just looking at the food and having it in the room. The next step is your tactile sense and being able to tolerate it with touch. Then you work your way up toward the face where you bring in the olfactory sense and see if you can tolerate the smell. Then you get closer to the mouth and see if the picky eater can touch it with their lips, lick it, taste it, swallow it. Moving through all these different senses at Project Play Therapy is done through creative play.

For example, if you are working with trying goldfish crackers, it would be, "Ohhh look at the cute little fishy in the lake. Let's give it a kiss and then put it back in the lake." You've just had the picky eater bring it up to their mouth to kiss it and they don't know the goal is to kiss it; they are just playing with food. Another example would be, "How far can you shoot the grape?" and again they are playing but your goal is to get them to touch the grape.

Sarah has worked with kids who started with eating only french fries, specifically from McDonald's, to progressing them to eat any kind of french fry, then to other variations of fried or cooked potatoes such as tater tots.

She said, "A lot of my kids think that a McDonald's cheeseburger is the only cheeseburger there is and even a cheeseburger made from Mom at home is too different of a cheeseburger to try at first."

To start you want to move toward something that is different but is still similar enough to a food the extremely picky eater is already comfortable with.

"I've seen kids improve in as short as a month, but I've also seen it take a year or more. It depends on how the family is able to implement the strategies we learn at home. With therapy meals, the goal is not calories or nutrition—it is engagement."

The more often a child is exposed to a new food the more likely they are to become comfortable with it. If the family is implementing a lot of the strategies they have learned repeatedly, the child will improve quicker.

Psychologist Elizabeth Phillips, whose research focuses on the psychology of tastes and eating, is the executive vice president and provost of Arizona State University. She was interviewed in an article called "The Psychology of Hating Food (and how we learn to love it)" and said, "Several factors help define our food preferences, adding that we can change the foods we enjoy if we so choose. It just takes a bit of time and effort."[13]

---

13 Bennington-Castro, J. (2013). *The Psychology of Hating Food (and How We Learn to Love It)*. [online] I09.gizmodo.com. Available at: https://i09.gizmodo.com/the-psychology-of-hating-food-and-how-we-learn-to-love-476720251 [Accessed 12 Jan. 2019].

Phillips says, "After birth, your preferences continue shaping for the next two years. Up until the age of two you will eat anything. But then you become neophobic—that is, you don't like new foods. So if you hadn't already been exposed to a certain flavor by the time you hit your terrible twos—whether through amniotic fluid, breast milk or solid food—chances are you won't like it."

At this point, most parents make a big mistake. "They think, 'Oh my child doesn't like this,' but it's actually ANYTHING new that they don't like," Phillips says. So parents typically stop trying to feed their child that food and the kid ends up apparently hating it for years to come. "They don't know that if they just keep giving it to their child, they'll eventually like it."

My mom checked my baby calendar and by four months I would grab the spoon from her and try to feed myself Gerber cereal. From five months to one year my mom and dad kept introducing new foods, and I ate peaches, pears, sweet potatoes, bananas, apple sauce and even chicken! However, right past one year old is when I started spitting the beef out and became pickier and pickier.

The key, then, is to make the food NOT NEW. Basically, you'll like a new or previously hated flavor if you're repeatedly exposed to it—studies suggest that it takes ten to fifteen exposures.[14] So if there's something you don't like, try it over and over and over again.

I had no idea about this statistic when I started trying new foods, but it is the same for extremely picky eaters at any age. Often, I noticed that once I started trying new foods around friends or family, they would ask, "Do you like it?" right after I tried it. If you have an extensive palate that you've developed over years, you can answer this right away. But at the beginning of developing my palate with all these new tastes and textures, I couldn't immediately answer that question.

I noticed I had to try something multiple times just to get used to it before I'd even come close to being able to answer the question of whether I liked it or not. I knew I could not gauge my like or dislike of a new food until I had tried it at least ten times. Only then, could I start to form an opinion about a new food.

Picky Points:

- Repeat, repeat, repeat. Repeatedly introduce new foods to extremely picky eaters until they are no longer new.

---

14 Birch, L., McPhee, L., Shoba, B., Pirok, E. and Steinberg, L. (2006). What kind of exposure reduces children's food neophobia?: Looking vs. tasting. *ScienceDirect*, [online] 9(3), pp.171-178. Available at: http://www.sciencedirect.com.

- The more often a child is exposed to a new food the more likely they are to become comfortable with it.

- It can take at least ten to fifteen tries for a picky eater to get used to a new food.

- Be patient and start with something similar to a food the picky eater is already comfortably with.

SWEET POTATO FRIES

———

Our next recipe is for roasted sweet potato fries. When you make a batch of homemade fries from one potato, it gives you a whole new awareness for just how many potatoes you are eating in one standard side order of fries out at a restaurant. It feels like most restaurants are giving you at least two whole potatoes worth of fries! These sweet potato fries will have the same shape we are used to with french fries but will have a slightly different taste with the sweet potato instead of a regular potato. We are keeping the texture similar to something familiar and trying a new taste. Just like the home fries these are better for you because you are roasting them in the oven with less oil than with a serving of deep fried french fries.

INGREDIENTS

1. 1 pound Sweet Potatoes
2. 2 tablespoons Cornstarch
3. 1/2 teaspoon Kosher Salt
4. 3 tablespoons Vegetable Oil

INSTRUCTIONS

1. Heat the oven to 400°F. Arrange two racks to divide the oven into thirds. Line two rimmed baking sheets with parchment paper if desired.
2. Peel the sweet potatoes. Cut in half lengthwise. Turn onto the cut side, then cut lengthwise into 1/4-inch wide planks. Lay the planks flat and cut lengthwise into 1/4-inch-thick sticks or wedges.
3. Place the sweet potato in a large zip-top plastic bag or bowl, add the cornstarch and salt, and shake or toss to combine until all the starch is absorbed into the sweet potato.
4. Coat the sweet potato in oil.
5. Divide the sweet potato among the 2 baking sheets and spread into a single, even layer, leaving space around each fry.
6. Roast until some of the fries are just starting to brown around the edges, about fifteen minutes. Remove the baking sheets from the oven. Using a flat spatula or turner, flip the sweet potatoes. Place back in the oven, switching the sheets between racks, and continue to roast until the fries are tender on the inside and crispy on the outside, five to fifteen minutes more. They will crisp up a little more as they cool.
7. Season with more salt if desired and serve.

PART 3

WHAT TO DO AND MODELING

We tend to model our eating behaviors on what we see others doing. So being aware that you're a role model for the picky eater in your life is important. We will go over some of the best strategies and practices for success with supporting an extremely picky eater and promoting healthy eating for your family. That includes understanding the role your environment plays, how to model healthy eating behaviors, how to relax and remove stress around eating, how to begin food chaining and how to build confidence with trying new foods.

CHAPTER 10

STUMBLING UPON
FOOD CHAINING

———

I started my picky eating blog back in 2012 to record my experiences with trying new foods, but I had actually been trying to expand my diet prior to that. I hoped that with the blog, other picky eaters might be able to benefit from my experiences as well. I didn't tell my friends and family about it for years. I was so ashamed of my picky eating and didn't want people to know how weird I really was.

At the very beginning, my steps were very small ones and it was all through food chaining (though I didn't realize it at the time) or linking one food I was really comfortable with to something similar that I thought was possible for me to try. It really started back in 2005 during my freshman year of college. I knew I wanted to expand my diet and my plan was to start out with foods that I already knew the texture but would have a different taste or vice versa, foods that I already knew what they would taste like but would have a different texture.

One of the first ways I tried to expand my diet was with chips because even with snacks I was picky. I used to only have Lay's potato chips or Tostitos tortilla chips. During college I started grabbing a couple of the other chip bags in the dining halls and then would try them later back in the privacy of my dorm room. It was the same idea here as with the ice cream. I already knew the texture but was just experimenting with new tastes. I distinctly remember when I tried Doritos for the first time and feeling like they were wayyyy too hot and spicy. When I tried Sun Chips the first time I immediately noticed they were extremely salty, with some chips way saltier than others, and I would only eat the less salty chips. Through this process, I experimented with taste. I found some new favorite snacks, such as Smartfood White Cheddar Popcorn, and some that aren't my favoirte too, such as Salt and Vinegar chips.

Now I realize that so far these have been mostly expansions in processed snacks but this started getting me used to the idea that I may be able to try new things and be okay. It was the beginning of my journey with trying new foods and it was a significant accomplishment.

In my junior year of college. I decided to try new bagels and cream cheese for the first time. Up until that point the only bagels I would eat were plain bagels with butter on them. The different bagels I tried went fairly well after quite a lot of repetition and I can now say I prefer sesame seed bagels and cinnamon raisin bagels over plain bagels.

The cream cheese was harder. The first few times I tried cream cheese I gagged. Have you ever noticed that sometimes there is a little liquid on top of cream cheese when you open a brand new pack and you have to mix that in? I certainly did because I wasn't sure if I should mix it in or just dump it out or if my cream cheese was even good and whether that's how it was supposed to be or not. For anyone wondering, you can just mix it in and it is fine.

With the cream cheese, it wasn't until I had it about ten times that 1) I could tolerate the texture of it on my bagel and eat more than one bite and 2) I could actually form an opinion on whether or not I liked the taste. Next time you have cream cheese notice how along with being creamy it is sticky and so when you take a bite it sticks everywhere inside your mouth. For an extremely picky eater who stuggled with texture it took quite some getting used to. I am glad to say that I can now have cream cheese on my bagels and both prefer and enjoy it!

I started trying different cheeses in college. Up until that point I would only eat Kraft American cheese, but I was able to try cheddar cheese in college which helped a lot with going out to eat at restaurants. It gave me the option to order a grilled cheese or a quesadilla at a restaurant and have something to eat besides just french fries. I also even tried some of the queso dip at Mexican restaurants as long as nothing else was in it besides the melted cheese. If there was anything else in it, I would be careful not to get it on my chip by dipping my chip only a tiny bit into the cheese.

College was the first time I found out there were other adult picky eaters out there in the world like me. My mom found an article, which she immediately sent to me, about a guy called Bob Krause, who had a website called www.pickyeatingadults.com and who was also an adult picky eater. Bob Krause is an extremely picky eater and runs a picky eater support community. I will never forget reading that article and going online to find out that I wasn't the only picky eater in the world. I was amazed at just how similar these other adults' picky eating diets were to my own.

I continued to make slow progress on my picky eating and expanded my diet a little bit throughout college. I graduated with a Quantitative Finance and Financial Economics double major and a minor in Mathematics and had been working a few years by the time I started the blog in 2012. That's when I really started to push myself again with trying new foods. Part of my motivation for really trying to expand my diet again was because I knew I wanted to have kids one day. I kept asking myself, "How could I be a good example for them if I couldn't even eat what I would ask them to eat?" I also felt as though my picky eating was a disadvantage in my work environment when client and coworker lunches were necessary. It unintentionally undermines your authority when all you order are french fries at a business lunch, and it felt like a huge hindrance and embarrassment at business events.

I kept food chaining with taking one food I was familiary with and either trying something that had a slightly different taste or texture, and I made good progress. I started trying different snacks and fruits and would write about what it was like trying each new food for the first time. It is like what a child would experience when they are first trying new foods, but as an adult I could express all the little nuances in taste and textures that many people no longer notice or think about when they are eating.

For example, have you really noticed all those little seeds on the outside of a strawberry and what that texture is like on your tongue? Have you thought about what it is like to eat soup lately? The strange combination of liquid and solid foods that you are eating while simultaneously experiencing the temperature of the food all at once? Have you noticed how much more you have to chew meat than fruit because meat is denser?

Although this wasn't the complete solution for me, I think especially while kids are young this type of food chaining can make a HUGE difference. Especially if you put the child in the driver's seat to decided what to try next—even if it is just a different type of ice cream or new bag of chips at first. The benefit it provides by building up their confidence and believing it could be possible to change is invaluable.

This went on for four years. I continued to food chain and try new foods but still felt handicapped at meals with coworkers or weddings for friends where I couldn't eat anything being served before I finally found Felix's therapy in 2016.

In 2006 there was a study called

"Food Chaining: A Systematic Approach for the Treatment of Children with Eating Aversion" written by S Cox, C

Fraker, L Walbert, C Mogren, C Swenny and M Fishbein.[15] They studied the efficacy of food chaining on children with extreme food selectivity. Extreme food selectivity was defined as an inappropriate limitation of food acceptance based on age and developmental stage. Standard treatment for extreme food selectivity is labor intensive and often includes hospitalization. Food chaining is an individualized, nonthreatening, home-based feeding program designed to expand food repertoire by emphasizing similar features (taste, temperature and texture) between accepted and targeted food items.

Ten children (five males and five females) aged one to fourteen that were diagnosed with extreme food selectivity between September 2001 and June 2003 were enrolled in a food chaining program for three months. The children had therapeutic sessions of a half hour to two hours per week. Rating scales were used to monitor the acceptance of modified food items. Interventions were provided through direct contact, telemedicine, telephone contact, voicemail, and electronic mail.

---

15 Fishbein, M., Cox, S., Swenny, C., Mogren, C., Walbert, L. and Fraker, C. (2006). Food Chaining: A Systematic Approach for the Treatment of Children With Feeding Aversion. *Nutrition in Clinical Practice*, 21(2), pp.182-184.

The results: food chaining led to an expanded diet IN ALL CASES. There were NO TREATMENT FAILURES.

Picky Points:

- Link and create association to foods/tastes/textures/smells that are already familiar.
- Start with simple foods that have only one taste or texture element...no tacos or salads to start.
- Start with dryer/less messy foods/that are whole pieces.
- Have the picky eater be involved in the preparation of food so they can see what is going into it.
- Empower them with the choice of what to learn about and try next.
- Try to involve another friend/teacher/mentor/grandma/peer to help your picky eater try something new.

CHAPTER 11

SET THE TABLE FOR SUCCESS

———

"There is the psychological aspect of food and the environmental aspect of food." ~David Schlundt

David Schlundt is an Associate Professor of Psychology at Vanderbilt University and has been a member of the Diabetes Research and Training Center since 1985. His area of interest is behavioral medicine with specific focuses on nutrition, behavior, and racial and ethnic health disparities. He is involved in developing and testing culturally competent approaches to weight loss, increasing physical fitness, and preventing relapses after medical and behavioral interventions for diabetes. His research has focused on social, emotional, and environmental influences on eating, exercise, and smoking behavior. He has looked into the effects of environmental factors on lifestyle behaviors and health disparities, the development and validation of behavioral assessment tools, and testing behavioral interventions. His current work examines how community action, public policy, and environmental change can be used to promote healthy eating and exercise.

David has been a vegetarian for twenty-one years now, which was triggered by his understanding of nutrition and health. He said, "After seeing study after study cross my desk showing negative side effects from eating meat, I simply couldn't ignore it."

David says, "If we look at how nutrition has been thought about in the past, it has been centered on just the one person. We need to take into account the environment that person is in as well. For example, think about Cassie the cat. Cassie is currently overweight. We ask the question, "Why is she overweight?" Well you could look at all of her individual characteristics. Perhaps it's because she's female or because she's pre-genetically disposed to gain weight. These could be factors, but really it's because the guy who feeds her is giving her a lot of food and she eats it. The vet recommends cutting back on how much food she is given at meal times and Cassie loses weight. Simple as that. It feels like it is way more complicated than that though."

David continues, "We really live in a different food world than we evolved to survive in. Hunters and gatherers would typically travel about seven miles a day and lived during times when there was both scarcity and when more food was available than needed. Our food environment today, however, is a giant corporate system that aggressively markets foods that are delicious and irresistible even though we are biologically engineered to survive in scarcity.

"You can't take the person out of the context," as David says. Not eating healthy and eating mindlessly are real problems but there are also so many external factors influencing our behaviors that we need to be aware of as well.

David says, "Keep in mind that when you go to eat in the real world, you are embedded in a context and that context has changed with the twenty-first century. Most people are not very mindful and are very susceptible to marketing. This development began during the WWII era when food started shifting away from the farm and became more of a manufactured item with the rise of TV dinners."

A study was conducted in June 2001 called "Eating behaviors and attitudes following prolonged exposure to television among ethnic Fijian adolescent girls" conducted by Anne E. Becker, Rebecca A. Burwell, Stephen E. Gilman, David B Herzog, and Paul Hamburg on how watching TV alters teenage girls' view of their body.[16] The traditional culture in Fiji encourages dinner guests to eat as much as possible. A robust nicely rounded body is the norm for men and women. "You've gained weight" is a traditional compliment and "going thin" is considered a cause for concern. But when the girls watched more TV with American television shows like *90210*, *Seinfeld*, *Xena* and *Melrose Place,* they quickly changed how they perceived their bodies. Of the sixty-three Fijian girls who were on average seventeen years old, the girls who watched TV three or more times a week were 50 percent more likely to describe themselves as "too big or fat" and 30 percent more likely to diet than the girls who watched TV less frequently.

David mentions, "The psychology of eating has to do with how people live, how they access food, what they eat, their food culture, and their food environment. Eating disorders stem from when things psychologically go wrong with your relationship with food."

"There are no bad foods but there are bad diets."

When asked about what some of the challenges are with eating healthier, David commented, "The fear of losing out

---

16 Becker, A., Burwell, R., Herzog, D., Hamburg, P. and Gilman, S. (2002). Eating behaviours and attitudes following prolonged exposure to television among ethnic Fijian adolescent girls. *British Journal of Psychiatry*, 180(06), pp.509-514.

comes into play and you have to ask yourself, 'What are you afraid you'll have to give up?' We need to get out of black and white thinking about food. You can have both brownies and a healthier diet.

"We are biologically wired to want foods that are high in fat, sugar and salt because they turn on the pleasure centers in the brain. That's why these are usually your 'comfort foods.' You don't hear about veggies as a comfort food," said David.

In a study that asked hypothetically if people would prefer fruit or chocolate as a future snack, 74 percent chose fruit. But, when those same participants were presented with both fruit and chocolate in real-time, 70 percent selected chocolate.

A person's actions can be dramatically influenced by related contextual features. For instance, research shows that kitchenware size significantly influences serving and eating behavior. In a series of studies, individuals who were given larger bowls served themselves between 28 and 32 percent more cereal than those given smaller bowls. Studies also report that people tend to eat 90–97 percent of what is on their plate, irrespective of plate size.[17]

---

17 Stulberg, B. (2014). *The Key to Changing Individual Health Behaviors: Change the Environments That Give Rise to Them | Harvard Public Health Review: A Student Publication*. [online] Harvardpublichealthreview.org. Available at: http://harvardpublichealthreview.org/

The 2005 study called "Bottomless bowls: why visual cues of portion size may influence intake" by Brian Wansink, J.E. Painter and J. North reflects just how those little environmental cues around us can affect our eating. The study used self-refilling soup bowls to examine whether visual cues related to portion size would influence the amount someone was eating without altering their estimated intake or satiation.

There were fifty-four participants, ages eighteen to forty-six years old that were put into two groups. One group was given an accurate visual cue of their food portion with a normal bowl and a second group was given a biased visual cue with a self-refilling bowl. The self-refilling bowl would slowly and imperceptibly refill itself while the participant was eating the soup at a modified restaurant-style table to accommodate the soup apparatus. The results were that the participants who were unknowingly eating from self-refilling bowls ate 73 percent more soup than the participants eating from the normal soup bowls!

What's also interesting is that they didn't believe they had consumed more, nor did they feel more sated (or full) than those eating from normal bowls. This study supports the notion that the amount of food on a plate or bowl increases

the-key-to-changing-individual-health-behaviors-change-the-environments-that-give-rise-to-them/ [Accessed 12 Jan. 2019].

intake because it influences consumption norms and expectations, and it lessens your reliance on self-monitoring. It seems that people use their eyes to count calories and not their stomachs. The importance of having salient, accurate visual cues can play a role in the prevention of unintentional overeating.[18]

In fact, not only can your environment influence your food intake, but it can also influence your intake of less palatable things as well.

In 2005 another study called "Bad Popcorn in Big Buckets: Portion Size Can Influence Intake as Much as Taste" was conducted by Brian Wansink and Junyong Kim. It is often believed that people overeat the foods they like. This study investigated whether environmental cues such as packaging and container size are so powerful that they can increase our intake of foods that are less palatable. In the study 158 moviegoers in Philadelphia were randomly given a medium or large container of free popcorn that was either fresh or stale (fourteen days old). After the movie, they measured how much each person ate of the popcorn and measured their perceived taste. Moviegoers who were given fresh popcorn ate 45.3 percent more popcorn when it was given to

18   Wansink, B., Painter, J. and North, J. (2005). Bottomless Bowls: Why Visual Cues of Portion Size May Influence Intake**. *Obesity Research*, 13(1), pp.93-100.

them in large containers. This container-size influence is so powerful that even when the popcorn was disliked, people still ate 33.6 percent more popcorn when eating from a large container than from a medium-size container. So even when the food is not tasty, large packages and containers can lead to overeating.[19]

You can apply this knowledge both to yourself and what you are eating but also with respect to what your family and picky eater is eating. Just as a smaller plate, bowl and cup will help you to eat and drink less so will a larger plate, bowl and cup cause you to eat and drink more.

The silver lining is if you want to encourage your family to eat more of a healthy vegetable or fruit and drink more water, use a larger bowl or plate and a larger cup to naturally increase the amount you'll consume of your vegetables and water. Same principle applies for those things you don't want to consume as much of like sugary drinks or chips. You can use smaller cups, bowls and plates to control your portion sizes.

Be aware of the eating environment you've currently created and how you can adjust it to improve eating and health in

---

19 Wansink, B. and Kim, J. (2005). Bad Popcorn in Big Buckets: Portion Size Can Influence Intake as Much as Taste. *Journal of Nutrition Education and Behavior*, 37(5), pp.242-245.

your household. What you buy in the grocery store and bring into your house impacts what you will eat. Make it easier on future you and set yourself up for success with healthy options.

If you are an extremely picky eater and want to expand your diet, make sure there are new foods in the house available to try and they are offered consistently. If you want to cook more often, make sure you have the cooking utensils and ingredients consistently on hand to make it easier when it's time for dinner. If you want a variety of different foods in your diet, buy a variety of food when you are at the grocery store. If you're trying to improve your health and relationships, eat at a table together with family or friends instead of in a car, in front of a TV, or at your desk.

While I was in Belgium, after my therapy with Felix, I learned the importance environment could play in my success. It was possible for me to try new foods. However, if I didn't consistently make an effort to have new foods available in the house it was less likely that I'd continue to try new foods. If I bought something new at the grocery store, even if I had no idea what to do with it, I was seven times more likely to try it. Simply because I had it readily available during the week. Unlike other nights, when I wanted to try something new, but would have to figure out what to get, run to the store, buy it, bring it home and prepare it all before trying it. Make it easy for yourself and build an environment that will set you up for success.

Picky Points:

- We are subconsciously affected by our eating environment.
- Your environment influences your food intake of both desirable and undesirable foods.
- We tend to eat 90–97 percent of what is on our plate, irrespective of plate size.
- Design your eating environment to help you and your picky eater succeed.

CHAPTER 12

MODELING MATTERS

———

"Parental modeling is so powerful, not only their food choices but also their attitudes about food. I think nutrition is as much a belief system as it is a science. People have such strong beliefs around food and nutrition. Our beliefs and attitudes are just as influential to our health, if not more so, than whether or not something has more vitamin C or Iron in it." ~Jamie Pope

Jamie Pope is an award-winning Assistant Professor of Nutritional Sciences at Vanderbilt University. Jamie holds a Master of Science degree in nutritional science and has worked in the areas of obesity research, weight management, health promotion, and heart disease prevention. Since 2000, Jamie has taught the science and scope of nutrition to Vanderbilt undergraduate students as they prepare for career and academic paths in not only healthcare, but a wide range of professions.

In 2013, she modified her nutrition courses at Vanderbilt and created the first Massive Open Online Course (MOOC) for introductory nutrition on the Coursera learning platform, which attracted more than 175,000 students worldwide. She has been published in the *Journal of Nutrition and Dietetics,* is a member of the Academy of Nutrition and Dietetics and has served as media representative for the Tennessee Dietetic Association, during which time she was named as Outstanding Dietitian of the Year for the Nashville District. Earlier in her career, Jamie co-authored several popular press books, such as *The T-Factor Fat Gram Counter,* which spent over three years on the New York Times best-seller list. Most recently, she co-authored *Nutrition for a Changing World,* an introductory nutrition textbook from Macmillan Learning and Scientific American that is used in over one hundred colleges and universities across the US.

When we first started talking, Jaime mentioned, "I teach college kids who are at an age where they are in transition with food and their eating environment. For most of their lives, there was food stocked in the kitchen and their dinner was provided for them. Now they are essentially 100 percent responsible for how to feed themselves in the college dining halls, social settings, and dorm rooms. I show a chart in an early class with the division of responsibility for feeding a child between the parent and child as they grow older. At age twelve it is about 50/50 in terms of responsibility between parent and child, but by college age it shifts to 100 percent of the young adult's responsibility.

"Parents are responsible to have a variety of healthy and nutrient rich options for their children at home. They are responsible for quality, frequency of meals, timing of meals, and availability of food, but the child, even from a young age, should dictate the quantity. Parents tend to override that by pushing children to clean their plate or eat more in order to have the reward of dessert. However, they should allow the child to gauge when they are full and learn to listen to their own body."

Jamie was assistant Girl Scout leader for her daughter's Girl Scout troop when the girls were all about eight or nine years old. One day they had been given free coupons for Cinnabon and took all the girls out to a large outlet mall in Nashville, Tennessee. One of the girls had a mother who was quite strict about allowing her daughter only organic food, yet this young girl was part of the troop. The Girl Scout leaders knew the mother's preference for organic food but also didn't want this child to feel left out and so they gave all the girls in the troop a coupon for a cinnamon roll.

Jamie said, "Most of the girls only broke off a few pieces or at most ate half of their quite large cinnamon rolls, but this young girl quickly consumed the entire thing. Not only that, she then tore apart the box and began licking any remaining icing off of the box. This was so profound to me. I realized this child was not prepared to deal with the 'real' world, which has Cinnabons in it. It made me ask, 'What is she going to do when she gets to college and is on her own and has to make decisions about food for herself?'

"It's the parents' responsibility to show kids balance, teach positive behaviors and model them, not just preach about them. Setting up a home environment that has a variety of all different kinds of food is important.

"One of my friends' displays what might be considered 'orthorexia,' which is an obsession or fixation with eating foods that one considers healthy and avoidance of specific foods that one might consider bad. She had an unhealthy relationship with her weight (she relishes it when others tell her she is 'skinny') and around what she ate or how much she exercised. I could see the impact her own relationship with her body and food was having on her daughter. It's really hard but we have to be aware of what we model to our children and our attitude around eating."

Keep in mind that the Academy of Nutrition and Dietetics at eatright.org has four characteristics of a healthy diet and overall good nutrition for kids:

1. Meets nutritional requirements for growth and development: consumes adequate amounts of overall energy and essential nutrients (vitamins, minerals, protein)
2. Helps prevent and reduce the risk of chronic diseases like obesity, heart disease, diabetes, and cancer
3. Promotes a healthy body weight with appropriate energy (calorie) intake for age and activity level
4. Fosters an appreciation and enjoyment of food

Jamie remembers going to a conference back in the eighties where there was an aerobics instructor in attendance who would comment on and critique what others were having for lunch. The aerobics instructor shared that a splurge for her was to have a nonalcoholic strawberry daiquiri once a year. Jamie confessed, "I didn't really want to eat out with her and feel judged. I love trying new foods and socializing over meals without the shadow of focusing solely on calories or 'perfect' choices."

If there was such a thing as "perfect" eating and if on a one to ten scale, perfect eating was a ten, Jamie said, "You don't want to be a ten. Nobody wants to hang out with a ten." Perfect is not the goal. A well-rounded diet that is healthy, nutritious and delicious is the goal.

Now dads, listen up. This is specifically for you! Your children, and your sons especially, are more likely to follow your food example than they are to follow their mom's.[20] (I know. I'm sorry, moms, but it's true.)

According to a 2016 study titled, "Family functioning and quality of parent-adolescent relationship: cross-sectional associations with adolescent weight-related behaviors and weight status" fatherly eating habits were one of the biggest influences over whether children grow up to be overweight or obese, especially for their sons. There were 3,768 females and 2,614 males in the study ages fourteen to twenty-four years old. They examined cross-sectional associations of family functioning and quality of mother- and father-adolescent relationships with adolescent/young adult weight status, disordered eating, intake of fast food and sugar-sweetened beverages, screen time, physical activity, and sleep duration.

---

20 Wright, J. (2017). *Father's Day PSA: your kids are what you eat.* [online] CBC News. Available at: https://www.cbc.ca/news/canada/new-brunswick/dads-eating-habits-1.4161796 [Accessed 12 Jan. 2019].

Eighty percent of participants reported high family functioning and 60 percent and 50 percent of participants reported
high-quality mother and father relationship, respectively.

They found that young adults reporting high family functioning and more positive relationships with their parents
reported better weight-related behaviors. Among both males
and females, high family functioning was associated with
lower odds of disordered eating, and, among females, lower
odds of being overweight/obese and eating fast food one or
more times a week.

The father-son relationship outweighed that of mother
and son as a determinant of future health, even when
mom was doing most of the food preparation, according to Wayne Hartrick, president of the Canadian Men's
Health Foundation.

"The children tended to mimic their father's eating behaviors more than their mother's," Hartrick said. "It's worth
fathers thinking about—kids are just quietly mimicking their
health behaviors."

Sometimes the best thing we can do is set a good example
with improving our own diet and lifestyle. Your children and
picky eaters pick up on everything, and they certainly pick up
on your food preferences as well. Your actions speak louder

than your words. It is ineffective to scoff at your broccoli and then tell your kids to eat it.

You have a huge opportunity to positively impact your child's food choices and preferences. Instead of trying to change their picky eating, try focusing on what you could improve first. When they see you enjoying your fruit smoothie as a treat they might want one too. When they hear you say you're excited for sweet potatoes tonight and actually mean it, they will be excited for them too. And faking it doesn't work. Your kids pick up so much from you and can tell when you aren't being genuine.

Picky Points:

- Take responsibility for the quality, frequency of meals, timing of meals, and availability of food in your home and let your picky eater dictate the quantity they eat.
- Model the balanced healthy lifestyle and positive behaviors you want to see from your extremely picky eaters.
- Perfect is not the goal. A well-rounded diet that is healthy, nutritious and delicious is the goal.
- Children tend to model their father's eating behaviors more than their mother's.

CHAPTER 13

RELAX AND DESTRESS

"Slowing down is key to learning that eating is fun." – Jennifer Peterson

In 2016, Jennifer Peterson worked with a two-year-old little boy who had Down syndrome. He would smash his food with his tongue to compensate for his lack of chewing skills. When he was given foods he could not smash with his tongue, he would just swallow them whole, which was not fun.

His mom and dad were unknowingly trying to get him to eat foods that he just wasn't ready for yet, such as gummy bears and Cheerios, because his chewing skills weren't fully developed. His parents were already dealing with so much: occupational therapy, physical therapy, speech-language therapy, leukemia...this was just one more challenge on their list. They were overwhelmed, stressed, and wanted to have their baby do one thing just like everyone else.

His mom kept trying to give him bread, but he couldn't chew it, so he would just spit it out. Mom would get mad and stressed out and put it back in his mouth, and he'd just spit it out again and scream and cry and throw everything on the floor. Then everyone was upset and stressed out and spiraled even further into a negative association with food. Eventually he just stopped eating all together because he learned that food is not fun.

So the parents came in to work with Jen, and she sat down and talked with them about what they could do to develop his chewing skills. Some of the chewing activities she recommended were things like giving him carrots so he could use his gums to munch on the carrot and encourage tongue lateralization.

Jen said, "If you think about a carrot stick, it is safer because it is a hard thing to slowly gum on. He has control and holds the carrot and brings the carrot to his mouth and isn't surprised by big pieces that he would have to swallow. I try to get it out of the mouth before it breaks off. Though I've had it break off a couple of times and the child will usually spit it out. He doesn't have to swallow it and can just get used to it. I also put dissolvable puffs on the molars to allow the child to work on chewing and tongue lateralization without having to bite down hard on something."

Other chewing activities and tools kids can try would be an ark chew or y chew during playtime, a mesh baggy with fruit in it to practice biting and swallowing the juice without any of the big pieces, and making silly and scary faces in the mirror with different tongue positions.

While building up his chewing muscles with carrot sticks, he was also allowed to feed himself purees. Now you have Mom way less stressed out because there is no fighting and arguing around food and the child is able to slowly learn how to chew and get comfortable with eating again.

Over time strawberries, bananas and other soft foods were added back into his diet. He developed more physically and cognitively (with the help of his physical therapy, occupational therapy and speech-language therapy) and he learned tongue lateralization after about two months. He was also munching after two months, eating soft solids after about three months (strawberries, french fries) and then moved on to medium solids (muffins, soft bread). After about twelve months, he was eating chewy foods (licorice, gummy worms).

In a stress and body composition study designed at Ghent University, 437 children (between five and twelve years old) were asked questions on stressful events, emotions (happy, angry, sad, anxious) and problems (emotional, peer, conduct and hyperactivity). Data was collected on the children's emotional eating behaviors and also on their dietary patterns: frequency of fatty foods, sweet food, snacks (fat and sweet), fruits and vegetables. Stressful events, negative emotions and problems were associated with emotional eating. Associations were also observed between problems and both sweet and fatty food consumption. Overall, stress was associated with emotional eating and an unhealthy dietary pattern and could thus contribute to the development of children becoming overweight.[21]

Make the eating environment a no-stress, no-anxiety, no-pressure zone. Eating should be enjoyable and relaxing, not stressful and nerve racking. If you feel yourself stressing out take a five-minute break to breathe deeply and re-focus yourself. Relax, meditate or just sit quietly with your eyes closed for a few minutes to destress. Go for a quick walk outside, stand up and stretch or move around for a few minutes to destress.

21 Michels, N., Sioen, I., Braet, C., Eiben, G., Hebestreit, A., Huybrechts, I., Vanaelst, B., Vyncke, K. and De Henauw, S. (2012). Stress, emotional eating behaviour and dietary patterns in children. *Appetite*, 59(3), pp.762-769.

I know that is much easier said than done sometimes but it is important. Especially when a phobia of food has been formed. There is a lot of fear and anxiety around food to begin with, so we need to create a relaxing and fun environment so eating food isn't such a scary and anxiety ridden place to be.

How can being around food be relaxing and fun and interesting again? Give children opportunities to be exposed to new things in an environment where they are comfortable with no pressure. Give them the opportunity to try a new food without being stared at or watched. Allow plenty of time for them to try something new, where there is no rush so they can study it for a little while if they want.

It wasn't until my family stopped making a big deal about my extremely picky eating that it was even possible for me to relax enough around food to begin being curious about it again. Even enthusiastic pressure can still sometimes be pressure. If I am considering trying something new and I know how badly you want me to try it, it'll still be hard to try it in front of you because I don't want to disappoint you and disappoint myself if it doesn't work. Sometimes even just giving a picky eater some options to try new things on their own or when people wouldn't be watching can be helpful.

Picky Points:

- Stress is linked to irregular feeding behavior, unhealthy dietary patterns and emotional eating.
- Remove the stress around trying new foods, cooking, and eating.
- Create a comfortable, relaxed eating environment with no pressure.
- Provide extremely picky eaters with plenty of time to examine something new without lots of watchful eyes.
- Give picky eaters control over the amount they want to try; start small.

HASH BROWNS

Now we are going to move to the frying pan with hash browns. Hash browns are a breakfast dish using a potato and can be varying degrees of crispiness depending on how they are cooked. Here we are trying a slightly different crispy texture by cooking them using the fying pan. We are creating a fried crust on the outside with a softer inside. Whereas with a french fry you have a lot of the crispy outside and just a little bit of soft inside there is a lot more of the softer inside with a hash brown. It is a different texture proportion of crispy to soft to get used to.

INGREDIENTS

- 3 Russet Potatoes
- 4 Tbsp Butter

- Salt
- Pepper

INSTRUCTIONS

1. Scrub potatoes (no need to peel or remove brown spots) and place in stockpot.
2. Cover the potatoes with cold, salted water and then bring to a boil.
3. Boil for about 10 minutes.
4. Drain and rinse potatoes with cold water until easy to handle. Remove any bruised or brown spots with a knife.
5. Using a box shredder or food processor, shred potatoes.
6. Melt butter in a large skillet or griddle over medium-heat (on the griddle we did 350°F).
7. Place potatoes evenly over the butter and cook until a golden-brown crust forms on the bottom (5-7 minutes). Flip potatoes and cook until crust forms on the other side.
8. Remove from heat and serve immediately.

PART 4

LEARN ABOUT FOOD AND COOKING

For an extremely picky eater, part of the process with trying new foods is learning about food and cooking. Even if a picky eater isn't ready to start trying new foods yet, he or she can learn about cooking and begin to spark his or her curiosity of new foods. We don't just wake up one day as expert chefs, knowing how to cook everything and what the perfect healthy diet is. The fact is we have to learn it. Eating and cooking are learned behaviors. We learn about food and what to eat from our family, friends, schools, and the media. In this section we will learn more about food quality, food culture, and begin learning how to cook. It's not as hard as you think and it is one of the best things you can do for your health. You just have to get started.

CHAPTER 14

LEARN AT THE FARMERS MARKET

———

"This is my invariable advice to people: Learn how to cook—try new recipes, learn from your mistakes, be fearless and above all have fun!" ~Julia Child

Place Flagey farmers market was right by my apartment next to the Ixelles Ponds in Brussels, Belgium, and soon become one of my favorite spots to go while I was living in Europe. It is this wonderful farmers market held every Saturday and Sunday morning and there is not only lots of fresh local food on the Place but there are also food trucks so you can grab something to eat and sit out in the sun and relax and socialize.

Some of my favorites were the sweet and savory creperie Ty Penty owned by a lovely French couple, the waffle truck for amazing Liege waffles, and the champagne and oyster truck where you sit out at a little table on the Place sipping on champagne and savoring fresh oysters. Right in the corner of the Place Flagey market there is a permanent stand and landmark called Frit Flagey, which has some of the best frites (french fries) in Brussels! Then surrounding the 1Place are several stores as well including my favorite bakery Fleur du Pain, which always had the best fresh baguettes and a Delhaize grocery store for anything you couldn't find at the farmers market. Every weekend I would go to the farmers market to buy most of my groceries for the week and carry them back to 1my apartment and up the stairs in my little bags.

I had my breakthrough with Felix in November of 2016 while I was in Brussels, Belgium and returned to America in October of 2017. During the remaining eleven months while I was living in Belgium, I had the opportunity to explore the European food scene. I was able to try new foods for the first time in my life and it was both incredible and frightening. Still, I was on a mission to be able to eat everything. So, in December I started trying as many foods as often as possible.

First, I began with foods that were easy to prepare raw like fruits and vegetables. I would try one small bite of the different fruits and vegetables at the farmers market, which made me very nervous at first because, although I was by myself, I was in such a public place. What if I couldn't swallow it? What if I had to spit it back out right there and embarrassed myself? What if I gagged and threw up all over the fresh produce? Thankfully none of that happened. I took a few things back out of my mouth and tossed them in the little garbage can, but other than that I was able to try everything with no ordeals. I soon grew to enjoy sampling small pieces of these new fruits and veggies I'd never had before and talk with the farmers (in my beginner French) about anything I didn't recognize.

I would buy something new at the market and then would take it home and figure out how to cut it up or cook it later during the week. I would research the foods that were new to me—like broccoli and bell peppers and asparagus—and make a plan to keep trying new things. To help with this, I had a food journal that my little sister Janelle (Nelly) got me where I would keep track of what I had eaten every day. I felt a huge sense of accomplishment every time I tried something new for that week!

A month into the plan I realized there were a lot of new foods that usually aren't eaten raw and must be cooked (such as eggs) and I had to figure out how to either prepare or cook them. My cooking skills consisted of being able to cook a grilled cheese and a quesadilla—pretty beginner level to say the least. So my food education began. It was time to start learning how to prepare and cook these new foods.

Most of the food in the grocery stores was labeled in French, so I learned about a lot of new foods in French and then would figure out what it was in English and how to cook it. When my parents came to visit me in Belgium, one of the first things I wanted to do with them was go to the grocery store. We would walk around the store, I would ask my parents questions, and they would point out different things I could try and explain how I could cook them.

When I first moved back to the States I was laughing with my friends over dinner as I tried to explain a dish that I made with aubergine and they were both looking at me like, "What?" and so I tried to explain. "You know the long purple vegetable?" and they realized what I was thinking of was an eggplant! I had never really talked about eggplant before moving to Belgium so I didn't realize I had learned the French word instead of the English word for it.

There are so many steps with learning about food and cooking that people forget about after they've been cooking for so long. It's hard trying to learn how to cook everything for the first time on your own. It takes a lot of preparation. You have to find a new recipe for what you are going to try, you need to make sure you've bought what you need to cook it, and then you have to actually figure out how to cook it. I was surprised that there wasn't more out there as a central place to start for beginner cooks who are really just trying to enter the culinary world for the first time.

For example, I wanted to try a bell pepper but I didn't even know how to cut it up. But don't worry, YouTube to the rescue. Next thing I knew I had cut it up, cooked it and tried a red bell pepper raw for the first time. Here are some of the steps involved in trying a red bell pepper.

Step 1 – decide to try a red bell pepper
Step 2 – buy a red bell pepper
Step 3 – learn how to cut up a red bell pepper
Step 4 – actually cut up a red bell pepper
Step 5 – try a raw red bell pepper

Then:

Step 6 – learn how to cook a red bell pepper
Step 7 – cook a red bell pepper
Step 8 – try a cooked red bell pepper

Another one I distinctly remember that I wanted to try was an egg. Eggs were one of the foods that I was often told to try as a picky eater because they would be good source of protein since I wasn't eating meat. I didn't eat eggs as an extremely picky eater either but was curious about them after having so many people recommend them to me.

But in order to try an egg I had to figure out how to cook it. So what did I do?

Well naturally I just googled how to cook an egg! I watched several YouTube videos and settled on one from Gordon Ramsay on how to cook eggs three different ways and then gave it a shot. By the way, it's hard to know if you cooked it the right way when you are trying it for the first time and have no one to tell you if that is what it's really supposed to taste like or not. That's when it helped to try something new with friends or at a restaurant so I had something to compare to and gauge what things really should taste like before I tried cooking them myself.

When I look back on it now, it seems like I went from eating barely anything to being able to eat everything, but it took me months and months of planning. Every week I would take my journal out at the beginning of the week and pick at least one or two new foods I would try that week. I had to make sure to get that new food at the grocery store, research how to cook it and then actually cook it. For trying new foods at restaurants, I had to venture outside of my comfort zone and order something completely unfamiliar and ask my friends questions about anything I didn't recognize on the menu. I had to put myself out there and admit to them my lack of skills with a fork and knife and laugh at myself when I did something silly or made a mess trying to figure out how to eat something new.

There were times when I struggled and would fall back to my safe foods for a few days or weeks. And that's okay because I never stopped trying. I pushed myself to keep buying things I was uncomfortable with and trying them when it would have been so much easier to just eat the same things I already knew and was comfortable with.

It took time for me to figure out how to prepare something new. If a recipe said it would take thirty minutes, I would double it knowing that with my new chopping and cooking skills, I should give myself a buffer. It also took a bit of a toll on my budget, spending a little more for food I might only try one or two bites of at a time. But it was all completely worth it being able to try so many new foods and make such incredible progress to get to where I am now.

Picky Points:

- Visit your local farmers market to learn about food.
- Try handling or sampling the fresh produce with your picky eater.
- Be consistent and determined to persevere.
- Trying new foods takes time, money and effort, but it is all worth it.
- Remember to laugh at yourself, you're learning and it is okay to mess up or make a mess.
- It's okay to take a break and eat your picky eater comfort foods sometimes.
- Let trusted friends and family in on what's going on. They'll be happy to help you.

CHAPTER 15

TEACH YOURSELF THE BASICS

"I feel like food is at the center of every part of my life."
~Charlotte Reilly

Charlotte received a duel Bachelor of Science in Kinesiology and Business Administration, majoring in Marketing and Sports Management. She earned her master's in Public Relations and has led digital marketing strategies for a variety of high-profile sports entities, food and fitness brands, governing bodies and advocacy organizations such as the PGA TOUR, USA Gymnastics, Polar, Barilla, H-E-B, FDA, BIO, A Fresh Look (educating on GMOs) and Mondelez International. Charlotte grew up very active as a competitive gymnast and varsity rower and has always been interested in health and fitness. She has coached both youth and high school gymnastics for more than fifteen years and is a certified yoga instructor. Charlotte is a self-proclaimed foodie who loves to cook and is interested in opening up a wine bar or vineyard in the future with her husband Jeff.

Charlotte said, "My family has a tradition of hosting an annual crab feast every summer. We'd always go down to the Wharf in DC (before it was built up) and buy bushels of Maryland blue crabs to bring home and steam. We'd sit on the patio, pick crabs, drink beer and catch up. It's one of my all-time favorite experiences. I love how it brings everyone together. It's about as authentic of a Virginia seafood experience as you can get. It encourages you to get real with your food and enjoy the company.

"There is a big social component to food—having people over, sharing a meal, helping prepare dinner and creating friendships. Showing love through food really starts at birth with a mother nursing her baby to provide the milk and nutrients it needs to be strong. Growing up there are other instances of this—anything from Easy-Bake Oven experiences in childhood to baking sweet treats as a way to show appreciation, encouragement and celebration—whether that be baking a birthday cake with your mom for a sister's birthday or brownies for a high school sports buddy before a big game. You may make soup for a sick friend or follow a Blue

Apron recipe with a college sweetheart as a date. These food experiences all stem from showing love. When I come home and cook for my family, I feel better. I want to nourish them and give to them. There is a bonding element in cooking. Shopping at the farmers market or chopping vegetables next to someone and then sitting down to dinner brings people together."

"Your first relationship as a human being is with food," says Richard Wilk, anthropology professor at the University of Indiana and head of its food studies program. "The first social experience we have is being put to the breast or bottle. The social act of eating is part of how we become human, as much as speaking and taking care of ourselves. Learning to eat is learning to become human."

Charlotte said, "When I was a kid, my mom would have us sit up next to her as she was cooking at night. It started at a young age, whether it was helping pick the dried spices out of the cabinet to add to spaghetti sauce or stirring whatever was on the stove. We were always right next to her 'helping.

"It wasn't until college that I really had to learn how to cook on my own, though. Something I decided to create for one of my college projects was a mini recipe book. My mom gave me some of the basics to start. If I was homesick or craving something, I'd call her up, get the recipe and instructions and add it to the book. I would also go out to eat and try different ethnic foods—Thai, Mexican, Indian, etc.—then figure out what I liked and try to replicate it at home. For a while I'd buy all these ingredients to experiment, and my food was going bad faster than I could eat it. So I started figuring out what I could make with what I had on hand before it went bad. I would just google the 4 ingredients I had in my fridge, see what allrecipes.com came up with and then just give it a shot.

"It's really all self-taught; you have to take a vested interest in learning about food and how to cook.

"Anybody could be a good cook. It's just about knowing what complements each other and experimenting.

"I think one of the biggest challenges when learning how to cook is the setup and understanding what your staple ingredients are. My basic go-to seasonings are salt, pepper, garlic, and onions. I also like to use various chili spice, Mexican spice, and Asian spices.

"Now as a busy working professional, I don't cook anything that requires a lot of time, and I've found it's always possible to eat something healthy quickly. All you need is a few pantry staples and spices, fresh produce and a protein."

Certified health coach Isadora Baum agrees, "The common misbelief is that cooking a healthy meal is too time-consuming, complex and expensive. Unfortunately, this hesitation can cause us to order something quick and greasy or to stick with meals that come in a box or can. However, cooking healthy recipes can actually be pretty simple, fast and delicious."

Charlotte says, "You are starting to see a shift in our generation from what we were raised eating. My mom used a lot of canned and frozen vegetables, pre-packaged flavorings or mix-ins and processed grains and dairy, but I don't use a lot of that stuff when I cook. I use fresher ingredients, especially when it comes to herbs, produce and protein. I strive for farm to table. I like to know where it comes from.

"I always buy whatever looks good, fresh and is on sale at the grocery store. You don't have to buy expensive crops to eat healthy. On average cooking a homemade meal can be as cheap as $2 a meal. Like a beef stroganoff. It's a five-ingredient, twenty-minute dish that you can buy all the ingredients for under $10 and can feed you for four to five meals."

According to Trent Hamm at The Simple Dollar, a personal finance blog, "The average American eats an average of 4.2

commercially prepared meals per week.[22] In other words, as a nation, we eat out between four and five times a week, on average. On average this number is even higher for young professionals working in the city. A lot of people eat lunch out every day, and that's not even including a grab-and-go breakfast or ordering in for dinner as well. However, this number equates to 18.2 meals in an average month eaten outside the home.

"What kind of money are we talking about here? The average American spends $232 per month eating meals prepared outside the home. Given that there's 18.2 meals eaten outside the home in an average month by the average American, the average meal outside the home costs a person $12.75.

"Let's assume you're averaging $4 per meal per person when prepared in the home even though we know it is possible for home cooked meals to be even less than that.

"If you were to simply prepare all your meals at home, you'd save yourself $8.75 for each of those meals. In other words, the average American would save $36.75 per person per week or $147 a month by moving their meals from restaurants to home-prepared meals.

---

22 Hamm, T. (2017). *Don't Eat Out as Often (188/365) - The Simple Dollar.* [online] The Simple Dollar. Available at: https://www.thesimpledollar.com/dont-eat-out-as-often-188365/ [Accessed 12 Jan. 2019].

Try cutting back a bit on eating out. Brown bag it to work an extra time or two a week, or prepare a nice meal at home with your family instead of heading out on the town. Your wallet will thank you."

You can not only improve your health but also save money by cooking at home a little more often. Eating out becomes more of a pleasure and a treat rather than the norm. I remember when I was little it was such a special treat to go to McDonald's after a doctor's appointment or out to the "cook-in-front-of-you" (Hibachi) Japanese restaurant because it was my sister's birthday (even though I couldn't eat most of the food).

Figuring out what staples you should have in the kitchen is extremely helpful to know when getting started with home cooking. It is different for everyone but here are a few common ones you may want to consider having on hand in your pantry.

Basic ingredients to have in the kitchen:

- Seasonings: salt, pepper, olive oil, vinegar, honey
- On your counter: lemons, garlic, onions, good bread
- In your pantry: oatmeal, pasta, rice, beans, potatoes, quinoa
- For baking: flour, sugar, baking powder
- In the fridge: eggs, butter, yogurt, milk, parmesan cheese

There are so many other kitchen staples you can add to your pantry. These are just a few to get you started. You will naturally find yourself customizing your pantry and seasonings to your tastes and preferences as well as discovering what you like to always have on hand. The idea is to have a few of the basics always available so that when you are cooking something at the last minute you can reach in your pantry or fridge, grab one or two other ingredients and make something quickly. For example, just grab eggs, butter, salt and pepper and you've got scrambled eggs in just a few minutes.

Picky Points:

- Experiment with what you have and start teaching yourself.
- Figure out your "go-to" staple ingredients.
- Stock your pantry and fridge with staple cooking ingredients.
- On average you can save $8.75 per meal when you switch to cooking from home.

CHAPTER 16

START WHERE YOU ARE

———

"I absolutely love seeing people be excited about new foods. My favorite thing was when someone would come back to class and say, 'I tried this.'" ~Kathleen Costello

Kathleen Costello is the Nutrition Education Coordinator for AmeriCorps Vista / Hunger Free America and the Meal Coordinator for the Nashville Food Project, designing nutrition education and healthy cooking curriculums as well as implementing nutrition classes and demonstrations at community partner sites. She has her master's in Nutrition Education from American University and volunteers with Nashville Cares.

Nashville Cares is a nonprofit organization south of Nashville that provides resources for people at risk for or living with HIV/AIDS. Nashville Cares hosts a healthy cooking demo each month to encourage nutrition education. At Nashville Cares a lot of the men and women in the class are used to eating a lot of deep fried southern food and are high risk for diabetes or other health problems.

oo--She was so excited one day when several months later one of the men came up to her and told her, "That was actually one of my favorite meals" from all of her cooking demos. For several months after that, they all called her Vegan Girl, which she thought was funny because, "I'm not even vegan or a vegetarian."

She emphasized, "Try new foods! I don't care if you don't like it. Just try it. You never know. You could discover something new you hadn't tried before that you really love."

She thinks one of the benefits of having cooking demos is being able to take a recipe and say, "I know this recipe can look confusing but here is what I'm actually doing." That's why I think cooking demos are really helpful because if people are willing to listen and can actually see what you are doing, it doesn't seem so overwhelming.

"Cooking doesn't have to be very formal and it doesn't have to be hard. If you don't have the red pepper that the recipe calls for, use a green pepper or a yellow pepper or just don't include it at all. That's okay. Experiment, have fun and think of it as a challenge."

She was very excited to have one person come to class after they prepared a peach balsamic chicken and tell her, "I didn't have any peaches but I did have some canned pineapples, so I made it with the pineapples and it turned out pretty good!"

She said, "It's very rewarding being able to switch people's perspectives about food, especially for a population where nutrition has such an impact."

As Maya Adam said, "Home cooking is a very practical solution to our modern health challenges that can be put into action almost immediately using whatever resources are available."

Kathleen mentioned, "I think the most important thing is attitude. I have picky eater friends or busy friends who are under time constraints, and they just don't believe me when I say they can cook. It can taste good and take less time. I think just being open-minded to the idea that it is possible to make food that is cost efficient, doesn't take too long and can still taste good would be a great first step. The first step is usually the hardest.

"It can be hard to go there mentally if you're new to cooking.

"I think education about food is so important and it blows my mind that it's not a priority for a lot of people."

Kathleen said, "When I worked at a first and second grade summer school program at Bethlahem Center some of the kids wouldn't try something until their teachers did. Just having an adult in your life who encourages you to try something new or to say that it's important can have a big impact."

Putting the effort into making nutrition a component of your life can not only benefit you but your children too just by association. Just hearing from an adult or teacher that this is important will influence the child.

As Kathleen continued, "I think it's important to meet people where they are."

"If you show up telling people to spend their week's worth of groceries on just four organic expensive ingredients in order to be healthy when they aren't even cooking yet, it isn't going to work."

"It's very easy to think buying ingredients is more expensive than going through the drive through, but if you learn how to use the ingredients you buy, it becomes way cheaper. For example, if you just bought a big bag of brown rice and potatoes, you could use them in lots of different ways. If you make something ahead of time, you can freeze it for later if you don't want to eat the same thing all week. Just giving people ideas for how to use all of their food is really helpful. Cooking food in this way can be very cost efficient.

"Cooking food at home can sometimes take a little more time, but you can spend forty-five minutes making a stir fry and then have it ready to eat for three days. I think meal planning is great if you are under a time constraint. Take some time on the weekends or whenever your schedule allows to prepare something ahead of time. I cook all day at work, so some days I don't want to come home and cook any more. I say, 'Okay. I'm just going to make pasta tonight, or I make a simple rice dish with zucchini.' You can cook pasta in under fifteen minutes. A breakfast scramble will only take ten minutes. I'll cook a big batch of risotto on Saturday with the goal of eating it Monday and Tuesday nights. It does involve a little thinking ahead, but if you make it a priority on the weekend, it can make your week a lot easier."

As Michael Pollan said, "One of the best predictors of a healthy diet is whether it was cooked by a human being or a large corporation."

Picky Points:

- Don't worry about following the recipe exactly. Have fun experimenting with different ingredients.
- Be open to the idea that cooking can taste good, be affordable and take less time than you think.
- Make nutrition a component of your life and let your kids know.
- Just start where you are and make one small change you trust yourself to complete.
- Be realistic with yourself. Don't try and completely overhaul your routine all at once.
- Start meal prepping. It will save you time and money.

CHAPTER 17

QUALITY AND SOURCE AFFECT TASTE

"Where your food has come from and when you are eating it is paramount. The flavor of your food is compromised when it's out of season. So it's important to eat seasonally for the most nutrients and the very best flavors. I think it's important for us to know what good is and to expose people to how great things can really taste. Cooking and tasting things in season is fantastic! The more access you have and the more education the better." ~Chef Paige Healy

Chef Paige Healy is Chief Creative Officer of family restaurant company HOUSEpitality founded and headed by her father, Kevin Healy. HOUSEpitality has grown to five different restaurants in the Richmond, Virginia, area. The culinary experience in their family continues with Paige's husband, Chef Gregorio Spinzo. Paige and Gregorio are the creators of a delightful farm to table experience called Dinner in the Field in Richmond, Virginia.

Dinner in the Field was inspired by summer nights in southern Italy. When Paige met Gregorio it was August 2013 while she was studying for her master's culinary program. One day she was walking down the Lungomare Falcomata along the Italian seaside and ran into what felt like the only other girl in Calabria and definitely the only other girl in Silverado that was between the ages of twenty-five and thirty-five, Elenia.

Paige said, "I was pretty much the only one in the town who spoke English at that point so I was excited to meet Elenia. She was really smart and we would frequently meet up for coffee. We'd always talk about these crazy Italian men. One day I saw her on the boardwalk walking with someone I hadn't met before so I winked and said, 'Elenia, good job. You found a great one!'

"She turned to me and said, 'Ew, that's my cousin, not my boyfriend. Do you want to meet him?'

"And I was thinking, 'Yes, but no I can't, but yes!' So Elenia set up a dinner for us to all hang out together and Gregorio and I pretty much hit it off. I was American, he was Italian and we both loved cooking so that summer I learned a lot of Italian and he learned English and we fell in love."

Paige and Gregorio decided to stay in Italy until October and then were in a long-distance relationship for that winter. The following summer Gregorio came over to America to see how he liked it.

While he was in America, they started working with a bunch of the local farmers in Richmond and started planning how they could create local dinners like the ones they loved in Italy.

Paige said, "We thought what better way to enter the community than with something we really love and hook up with local farmers and connect people throughout the Richmond area."

Paige described what it was like to me, "In Calabria it's really hot and feels like it's 100 degrees during the day. There is no air conditioning inside and so for dinner you eat at dusk outside while the sun is setting as it starts to cool off with a nice slight breeze. Gregorio is one of eight children, so when his extended family got together, dinners could often be really large with as many as thirty-five people. Before dinner everyone would be doing something to help out. Either in the garden cutting up cucumbers and salting them with a little oregano or olive oil, or waiting for the pasta to be cooked, or getting the meat on the grill, or cooking the eggplant that they preserved, or cutting up the salami they have from the pig they slaughtered during the winter.

"It's all this amazing Calabreze food that is just hours or minutes off the vine and they're all sharing it out in the fresh air at this family style table out in the garden. It is magical," said Paige.

When Gregorio decided to move to America it was with his sister, Noemi, and his cousin, Matteo. The first dinner in the field Gregorio and Paige prepared was in June 2014 and it was just the four of them hosting with two other people from the restaurant who helped out, Carolyn and her son Chad. It was a hit right from the start and really just blew up.

Paige said, "We really invite people to be a part of our family and live the Italian lifestyle. Wine is on the table, we welcome everyone with Prosecco and start with an aperitivo. You're treated like family here so you can ask me anything about recipes and cooking, but I might also ask you to jump in and give me a hand with serving or grabbing something.

"We would talk about the food and explain how we are going to serve food that is just hours off the vine. We would also always make a point to take a moment and eat something that was just minutes off the vine. We'd ask the group to go harvest something from the garden directly and they'd pick their own fresh basil or fresh cherry tomatoes to taste. You get the full nutrients and sugar of the food this way, which also gives it such great flavor. The second the food is picked from the vine it starts losing those nutrients and sugars, which means it also starts losing some of its flavor.

"The source of what you eat and the timing of when you eat it is so important," Paige told me. She described how it would be rare to eat broccoli in the summertime in Calabria and that you wouldn't be able to find or eat watermelon in the wintertime.

Paige notes, "There is a high demand from the Calabria public for good quality. They aren't going to even tolerate it unless it's the best."

She laughed and said, "I always forget how much I like tomatoes until I eat them in August. In the past I've said I don't really like tomatoes, but really it's just that I don't like tomatoes when they are out of season. When they are in season I love them. There are so many things I had this perception of not really loving until I had it the way it was supposed to be eaten—fresh, grown regionally, and in season."

Start asking where your food is coming from. Ask the farmer at the farmers market. Ask you grocer. Research where your grocery store sources their food from. Learn what foods are in season in the spring, summer, fall and winter. Whatever is in season will also be less expensive at the farmers market and at the grocery store because they will have a larger supply of that produce.

Picky Points:

- The quality of your food not only affects the taste, but it also has more nutrients and is healthier for you.
- Take some time to figure out where your food is coming from.
- Eat seasonally for better quality, taste and nutritional benefits.
- Create your own dinner in the park, cook together, eat together and enjoy together.

CHAPTER 18

LEARN WHAT GOOD
IS AND DEMAND IT

―――――

"This food is not so much the fault of the Chef as it is the fault of the people who have accepted it. Do people accept it and say nothing because they actually think it is good?" ~Chef Patrice

Chef Patrice's mission is to be part of the change by educating people to know what good food is and how to produce good food—to give every lover of cooking the opportunity to immerse themselves in the joy of cooking and learn the techniques for truly cooking like a professional chef!

As he said, "It's about educating everybody."

One night, Chef Patrice was at a friend's wedding in Chicago which was hosted at a restaurant. For dinner at the wedding, they were served green beans from out of a can, pasta that was ten times overcooked and a chicken he said was so dry he wouldn't have served it to his dog. After cooking for as long as Chef Patrice has, he can immediately tell the difference between fresh and canned vegetables and good quality produce! His shock at this meal was apparent when he said, "I'm sorry, but in prison they eat better than this."

Chef Patrice is one of the most successful and well-known chefs in America with over four decades of culinary experience under his belt. He cooked for the White House for over fourteen years to "Americanize" the White House cuisine, served as Executive Chef at the French Embassy for over twelve years and was Chef at several leading French restaurants in Washington DC. He competed in prize-winning teams on Food Network television shows such as Iron Chef America and Food Fight. He holds his culinary degree from the prestigious Ecole Hôtelière de Marseille in the south of France. In addition, he has served as the Program Director for one of the nation's top ten culinary schools, "L'academie de Cuisine," in Gaithersburg, Maryland, where he has taught hundreds of chefs, many of whom have become very successful professional chefs in the culinary world.

He said, "In the previous generation, you didn't have to be a chef to know how to make some nice dishes. This was usually passed down from generation to generation."

With millennials eating out so much more, they aren't cooking at home as often. People won't even try something new unless it's presented to them. The supermarkets could help with this by stocking additional produce and providing guidance for how to cook with it. For example, you might notice at some grocery stores like Publix, they have recipes on display that you can take home with you. Trader Joes or Whole Foods have suggestions for how to cook the ingredient on the price label.

Chef Patrice said, "I went to the grocery store one day and there were only three sad little turnips available. I could tell they'd probably been sitting there for a while when the cashier didn't know how to ring them up because they are bought so infrequently. There are so many great things we can cook with turnips, but who wants to when they are probably old. If people were exposed to turnips in new ways or given recipes or suggestions to try, this could change."

One day, as a nice gesture, to spare Chef Patrice from feeling like he needed to cook something else after cooking all day, his wife bought a food tart at one of the local grocery stores. Chef Patrice could tell it wasn't going to be good just by looking at it when he got home.

"The dough wasn't cooked right. Sure enough, when we cut into it, the dough wasn't cooked through and it didn't taste very good."

Chef Patrice said, "We should go back to the grocery store and say, 'Look, this is not good. I'd like to return this tart.'" It's not about the money. It's about the principle that if we return the tart, the chef will get the message that he or she should do something different. It will bring awareness to the department that this is not acceptable and they will have a conversation about what to do about it. Any good manager at a grocery store will do anything they can to please the customer. They will notice if people are bringing their pies back, and they will stop selling them until they improve them."

In the words of Chef Patrice, "Americans need to refuse to buy the crap.

"People put a lot of importance on food in Europe; it isn't just about eating. It's also about socializing, the experience and spending quality time together. Food is a very important part of each country's culture and everyone expects good quality."

Marco Bolasco, editorial director of Slow Food and an Italian food expert says, "Food in Italy is love, then nutrition, then history, then pleasure. An Italian child's first experience with food is not buns or rice or eggs, but probably ice cream."[23]

But in America it isn't like that. Quality is harder to find and there is a lack of good cooking technique. The quality of the food that is carried both in the farmers market and in the grocery stores in Europe is better. This is what people are so drawn to when visiting and experiencing the great food in Europe. When you come back to America and see the difference in quality, as Chef Patrice puts it, "You just want to cry."

"In France we love food and enjoy food; food is pleasure," said Mireille Guiliano.

Lidia Bastianich said, "There is a history to Italian food that goes back thousands of years, and there's a basic value of respecting food. America is young and doesn't have that."

Did you know that yogurt has two whole aisles devoted to it in most European grocery stores, but there are usually just a few options in American grocery stores? Good quality

---

23 Choi, A. (2014). *What Americans can learn from other food cultures.* [online] ideas.ted.com. Available at: https://ideas.ted.com/what-americans-can-learn-from-other-food-cultures/ [Accessed 12 Jan. 2019].

should be expected both of the food itself and of the food that is being cooked and provided to us.

After teaching at L'academie for more than a decade, Chef Patrice decided to fulfill his dream to make the home chef a better cook and established "Cooking Live" as an online cooking school designed for anyone who wants to learn how to be a better cook.

One of his students cooked at home and was a good cook already, but she wanted to learn more. She took his classes every Saturday and is now cooking the dishes at a professional level with great technique and also understands the chemistry behind cooking.

One of his students said, "Cooking Live makes it so easy for me. Ever since taking cooking classes, I've become so much more confident in the kitchen. I'm much more efficient. I manage my time better. I work cleaner, and cooking has just become so much more enjoyable. It's about having fun in the kitchen. What I love about Cooking Live is it's such a new and different cooking experience. It's not only working in my own kitchen with my own tools, but I have an instructor right there with me coaching me through a new recipe a new dish. It's not just about the recipe. It's also about the technique I'm learning."

He has seen people become great cooks when they feel like they have the support they need and someone takes them by the hand and shows them step by step what to do. He wants to not only educate us about cooking but help us understand what good food is, learn how to cook better tasting food, have fun and be creative in the kitchen and ultimately just "enjoy cooking for your soul."

With so much information available at our fingertips online, there is ample opportunity for us all to learn how to cook anything we want. You aren't limited by what your parents taught you or just one style of cuisine. Now, you can find almost any recipe online and there are lots of YouTube videos and cooking classes you can enroll in! It's much easier than going off just the recipe cards your family wrote down for you.

Picky Points:

- Learn where your food is coming from and what good quality food is.
- Refuse to buy crappy food. Put your dollars behind good quality produce and restaurants.
- America's food culture is young and could learn a thing or two from other established food cultures.

POTATO PANCAKES

———

Now we will take a look at my Dad's potato pancakes recipe. We are going to use the frying pan again. Pancakes were a familiar and comfortable thing I was able to eat as a picky eater. These potato pancakes feel a little more familiar because they are formed and cooked the same way pancakes are. For these we have the same crispy texture on the outside with the soft texture on the inside. We are also venturing out and changing the taste slightly by adding in a couple of extra ingredients this time.

INGREDIENTS

- 1 Baking Potato
- 1 Egg
- 1/2 White Onion

- 1/4 cup of Milk or Cream
- 2 tbsp of Parsley Flakes
- 1/2 cup of Flour
- Salt
- Pepper

INSTRUCTIONS

1. Wash and dry the potato.
2. Cut into smaller pieces.
3. Blend potato, egg, onion, milk, parsley, salt and pepper together.
4. Pour in a bowl and add 1/4 cup of flour.
5. Heat up vegetable oil, duck fat or canola oil in a frying pan so it's sizzling.
6. Take a spoonful of the potato pancake mixture and drop into the pan to create pancakes.
7. Fry them until they are golden and crispy on each side.
8. Add a little salt on top when you take them out and enjoy!

PART 5

OUR RELATIONSHIPS WITH FOOD

Everyone has an individual relationship with food that starts forming when he or she is young. No two people have the exact same relationship with food, just like no two people are exactly the same. This section explores the science behind our relationship with food, how we can be more conscious of this relationship and why it develops the way it does. We are going to learn just how early our relationship with food begins, what being "healthy" really means, how our emotions are tied to our food and the role food beliefs play in our health. This is important knowledge for all of us to understand, whether we are extremely picky eaters or not.

CHAPTER 19

FROM BIRTH

—

Remember Jen.

Jen Peterson is a speech pathologist and has been working with young children and their families for over seven years. Jen works on infant feeding with new moms and their babies at a children's hospital in San Diego, California, to evaluate and treat children with a wide variety of complex medical diagnoses.

She was called in because a mom was having trouble feeding her four-month-old baby.

The mom was told, "You can't leave the hospital until the baby has gained weight for three consecutive days in a row."

You can imagine how the new mom's face would tighten with stress at that statement.

The pressure on any new mom is a lot to begin with, and now she's being told she is accountable for her baby's ability to leave the hospital.

More pressure.

Every time the mom tried to feed her baby boy, the baby would arch and pull away from her. The baby had a premature birth and had low tone and trouble managing mom's milk flow. He would cough and choke and gurgle and you could tell it was difficult for him. Since breastfeeding wasn't working she tried feeding him from a bottle instead but he was still coughing and pulling away from her. Of course this was stressing mom out because she was a new mother and already starting to blame herself for everything. She felt horrible because she was having trouble with breastfeeding her baby boy. Now she couldn't get him to eat from the bottle either and it just becomes this spiral. She got more stressed out with each failed attempt, the baby picked up on the stress from mom and was even less likely to want to eat, which in turn stressed out mom again.

No wonder our new mom's baby is having trouble eating with all that stress around.

✳✳

"Hey, guys. Let's relax!"

Jen stepped in to help and sat down with the mom. She put on some nice music, lowered the lights, watched the baby and helped Mom calm down and finally relax.

Mom had a good supply of breast milk so they decided to have Mom provide the breast milk via the bottle. Jen put a smaller nipple on the bottle so that it would slow down how quickly the milk was coming out of the bottle. She said, "We tried having her pump a little bit before feeding to slow down the flow but he still couldn't manage from the breast. He did better with the bottle and drank the whole thing with no coughing." Mom decided to use the bottle and would try breast feeding intermittently and would stop when he coughed.

Once they removed the stress from Mom and decreased the amount of milk coming out of the bottle, the baby relaxed and was able to eat. He then gained enough weight to go home from the hospital.

Research has shown that humans can develop these positive or negative associations with food at a very young age, even as early as during our first few times drinking from a bottle or a breast. Stress around food can affect young children's eating behaviors, whether from too much food at once or from Mom and Dad yelling at each other during dinner time.

My mom personally remembers being stressed out when first learning how to breastfeed me as well. She developed a breast infection with a fever, and it made it very difficult and painful for her to breastfeed me while I was little.

Understanding children's eating attitudes and behavior early is important in terms of children's health. Evidence indicates that dietary habits acquired in childhood persist through adulthood.

According to a study called "Influences on the Development of Children's Eating Behaviors: From Infancy to Adolescence," the first year of life is a period of rapid physical, social and emotional growth, during which eating patterns also develop.[24]

The first three years of life are a particular challenge because a child's feeding abilities and needs change with motor,

---

24 Birch, L., Savage, J. and Ventura, A. (2007). Influence on the Development of Children's Eating Behaviors: From Infancy to Adolescence. *Can J Diet Pract Res*, [online] 68. Available at: https://www.ncbi.nlm.nih.gov/pmc/articles/PMC2678872/ [Accessed 12 Jan. 2019].

cognitive and social development. In the first stage (birth to three months) of self-regulation and organization, the child integrates experiences of hunger and satiety to develop regular feeding patterns.

In the second stage (three to seven months), the infant and parent form an attachment that allows them to communicate with each other and the infant develops basic trust and self-soothing behaviors.

In the third stage (seven to thirty-six months), the child gradually "separates" emotionally from the parent and discovers a sense of independence or autonomy, making use of developing motor and language skills to control the environment and establish independent feeding.

During these first three years, infants transition from consuming a single food (i.e., breast milk or formula) to consuming a variety of foods more characteristic of an adult diet. This transition allows infants to learn about food through direct experience, as well as through observation of others' eating behaviors. Data indicates that breastfeeding and parental modeling in the toddler years play significant roles in establishing longer-term eating behaviors. Children are learning what, when, and how much to eat based on cultural and familial beliefs, attitudes, and practices surrounding food and eating. Parents and caregivers play a vital role in structuring children's early experiences with food and eating.[25]

Infants are predisposed to pleasing flavors. Shortly after birth, infants express preferences for sweet tastes and reject those that are sour and bitter. Preferences for salt are apparent at approximately four months. These predispositions are thought to have evolved to serve a protective function by encouraging the consumption of energy-rich foods (often signaled by the sweet taste) and discouraging ingestion of toxins (signaled by bitter and sour tastes). These taste preferences are unlearned and become very apparent to parents once infants begin the transition from exclusive milk feeding to a modified adult diet. In general, sweet foods such as fruits, flavored yogurts, and juices are readily accepted by infants while foods such as vegetables, which are not sweet, and may contain bitter components, are initially rejected. Laboratory studies have confirmed that young children readily form preferences for flavors associated with energy rich foods. Even the fruits and vegetables most preferred by children (e.g., bananas, apples, potatoes, and peas) tend to be those that contain the most energy.

---

25 Savage, J., Fisher, J. and Birch, L. (2007). Parental Influence on Eating Behavior: Conception to Adolescence. *The Journal of Law, Medicine & Ethics*, 35(1), pp.22-34.

Alternatively, children's acceptance of foods that have less initially pleasing flavors (such as vegetables) are shaped by their experience with those foods. Children decide their food likes and dislikes by eating and associating food flavors with the social contexts and the physiological consequences of eating them. The tendency for children to initially reject new foods is often just a case of neophobia (extreme or irrational fear or dislike of anything new, novel, or unfamiliar).

Several studies have demonstrated that children's preferences for and acceptance of new foods are enhanced with repeated exposure to those foods in a noncoercive setting. New foods may need to be offered to preschool-aged children ten to fifteen times before acceptance occurs. At the same time, simply offering new foods will not necessarily produce liking, but having children taste new foods is a necessary part of the process. Awareness of this normal course of food acceptance is important because approximately one quarter of parents with infants and toddlers prematurely drew conclusions about their child's preference for foods after two or fewer exposures.

The Feeding Infants and Toddlers Study (FITS), which provided data on the dietary patterns of 3,022 infants and toddlers, revealed that four- to twenty-four-month-old children typically consumed significant amounts of developmentally inappropriate, energy-dense, nutrient-poor foods. Of particular concern was the finding that 18 to 33 percent of infants and toddlers consumed no distinct servings of vegetables on a typical day and when vegetables were consumed, the most common choice was french fries.

Additionally, reported energy intakes exceeded requirements by 10 to 30 percent. Unfortunately, there is also evidence that these patterns tend to persist throughout childhood and into adolescence, and that diet quality tracks and declines from early childhood through adolescence.

The Canadian Community Health Survey (CCHS) suggests that seven out of ten children aged four to eight years fail to meet the minimum number of servings for vegetables and fruit in Canada's Food Guide to Healthy Eating. These children also fall short of reaching the recommended servings for grains and milk products, thereby suggesting that poor eating habits among children are endemic.

The obesity epidemic, which affects an estimated 10 percent of American children age two to five, is rooted in poor eating habits that begin between twelve months and twenty-four months, a new study presented at the annual scientific meeting of The Obesity Society has found.

Whether it has to do with picky eating, overeating, eating disorders or just overall health, there is a clear link between our eating behaviors as children and the effect those behaviors play later in life. My food phobia formed when I was very young, at just thirteen months old, and continued to affect me for the next twenty-eight years. Our relationship with food begins developing as soon as we are born and continues until we die. Take some time to really understand yours and ensure that you are encouraging healthy relationships with food for the loved ones in your life.

Picky Points:

- Reduce feeding volume and speed for infants if they are showing signs of distress when eating.
- Eating habits are developed early—between twelve and twenty-four months and sometimes even earlier.
- It is important to create positive associations and prevent negative associations with food for your children early on.

CHAPTER 20

WHAT IS "HEALTHY"?

———

"The way I see it, we should try not to label food so black and white. Learn about what emotional eating is, learn about what true fullness is, and learn about hunger cues. Sitting for twenty minutes after a meal and reflecting is important. Slow down during mealtime, sit down, plate it, and taste it, bite by bite." ~Rachel Fitzgerald

Rachel Fitzgerald is a professional counselor with a focus in treating eating disorders; she has worked at various treatment facilities and continues to work with women who have different eating disorders such as anorexia and bulimia. She is working and talking with women every day about their relationships with food.

When growing up, her mom was always the cook in their house, and Rachel was glad to have grown up with a pretty healthy relationship with food. Her mom made sure they always had a nice rotation of meals in their diet like flounder, spaghetti, beans and rice, and taco night.

Rachel's younger brother was a picky eater growing up. She remembers when he was young he would spit out his baby food. His diet consisted of toast, pizza, chicken nuggets, and cereal. Her mom, like mine and so many others, worked really hard to have him try new things. Rachel said, "It wasn't until he got a little older and was in middle school where something just switched for him and he started trying new and different kinds of food on his own and exposing himself to new foods."

Rachel was exposed to home cooking and many foods early on, but it wasn't really until she went to college in 2012 that she started to personally connect with food and have more of her own relationship with it.

Rachel said, "I think my relationship with food changed during my college years because I became more interested in cooking and for the first time I was not getting food from my family or from the dining hall. I really had to learn how to put meals together for myself (or with the help of my roommates). I happened to live with a good friend at the time who really enjoyed cooking, and I learned a lot from her. The social part of cooking with roommates was fun."

Rachel's friends were an integral part of developing her relationship with food and learning how to cook. Her roommates exposed her to beets and other new foods for the first time and she learned lots of new recipes from them.

As she put it, "Cooking becomes a really fun social thing when you are all doing it together." There is one day in particular she remembers where it had been a really rainy week, so she and her roommates decided to make a family dinner. She said, "We made these beer and cheese soup bread bowls and snuggled up on the couch afterward and had a movie night. It was one of the times that all five of us (me and four other women) were all cooking and enjoying food together. It was a comfort meal and it was so fun!"

She continued, "I feel that I have always had a pretty good relationship with food, but there was a shift in my interest in cooking and putting meals together for myself and friends during my college years. Everyone needs human connection and food is a key way humans can connect with one another." Rachel recommends to try and eat with friends, family or someone for every meal.

When I asked her how she wound up treating eating disorders, she said, "I really fell into it. I was really passionate about working with and empowering young women around topics like women in the media and body image and I landed a job working in a treatment facility. I am passionate about food and believe it can add so much pleasure and enjoyment to life. However, if that relationship is hurting, it really distracts and takes away from life. I am passionate about helping people to heal their relationships with food."

Rachel mentioned, "I think the media and diet culture can be harmful for clients who didn't get a lot of nutritional information growing up." Working with women with eating disorders Rachel has seen many women who are trying to change their relationship with food. Some of her clients are as young as eleven or twelve and already have such a negative association with food and their bodies.

Our education about food can come from several places: our family, our friends, our schools and the media. Right now a lot of our education around food comes from the media with advertising or the latest dieting trend. It can be very overwhelming and confusing trying to figure out what is healthy, what is not, and which diets to follow or cleanses to try.

At the treatment facility, they try not to use the words "healthy" and "unhealthy" so there is no labeling of food as either good or bad. For example, Rachel had one client who had labeled apples as healthy but almost everything else as unhealthy. Her client was eating a lot of apples every day, but she had reached a point where her bowel movements were no longer normal.

In her case Rachel said, "It would actually be 'healthier' for her to eat a brownie than another apple at that point to get some of the other nutrients her body needs."

But it can be tricky. "Many of us are not taught how to manage our emotions and when seeking or experiencing those feelings of comfort, love, pleasure, excitement, pain, or fear, we will look to food to short circuit those emotional experiences."

Awareness and eating mindfully is important, especially when you're faced with various emotions. Feel and be aware of your stress, anger, frustration, guilt, sadness, excitement when it surfaces and ride it out without turning to food to address it.

Rachel said, "I feel like so much of it comes from in the home. I think it's great for parents to expose their children to all types of food. Diet culture is so strong right now that there is always a latest trend or focus on restricting and cutting out certain foods or food groups. This diet culture can lead to kids starting to label foods as 'bad' and 'good' and can distract from learning how to respond to their hunger cues, honor their cravings, and have a positive relationship with food. Parents working on food education with their kids when they are young can make a big difference."

So how do we figure out what "healthy" or "normal" eating really should look like?

Ellyn Satter a recognized authority on eating and feeding, pioneer of the Satter Feeding Dynamics Model and Satter Eating Competence Model, and author of Division of Responsibility in Feeding says it well.[26]

She states:

- "Normal eating is going to the table hungry and eating until you are satisfied. It is being able to choose food you like and eat it and truly get enough of it—not just stopping because you think you should.
- Normal eating is being able to give some thought to your food selection so you get nutritious food but not being so wary and restrictive that you miss out on enjoyable food.

26 Tartakovsky, M. (2018). What Is Normal Eating?. [online] World of Psychology. Available at: https://psychcentral.com/blog/what-is-normal-eating/ [Accessed 12 Jan. 2019].

- Normal eating is giving yourself permission to eat sometimes because you are happy, sad or bored, or just because it feels good.
- Normal eating is mostly three meals a day, or four or five, or it can be choosing to munch along the way.
- It is leaving some cookies on the plate because you know you can have some again tomorrow, or it is eating more now because they taste so wonderful.
- Normal eating is overeating at times, feeling stuffed and uncomfortable. And it is under eating at times and wishing you had more.
- Normal eating is trusting your body to make up for your mistakes in eating.
- Normal eating takes up some of your time and attention but keeps its place as only one important area of your life.

"In short, normal eating is flexible. It varies in response to your hunger, your schedule, your proximity to food, and your feelings."

According to the 2013 National Eating Disorders Association Survey of Eating Disorders on The College Campus, full blown eating disorders typically begin between eighteen and twenty-one years of age. Out from under the watchful eye of parents and family, eating attitudes and behaviors can change and even become dangerous without anyone noticing.[27]

Social pressure to make friends, have romantic relationships and achieve academically can lead to maladaptive coping mechanisms in the form of disordered eating. Our current cultural climate idealizing thinness and placing emphasis on weight as a primary indicator of health only contributes to fears of gaining weight. Although some students will experiment with dieting and escape unscathed, 35 percent of "normal" dieters progress to pathological dieting. Of those, 20–25 percent progress to partial or full–syndrome eating disorders.

Anorexia is the most lethal psychiatric disorder, carrying a six-fold increased risk of death, FOUR TIMES the death risk from major depression. According to an article in *Psychology Today* called "The Deadliest Disorder," people with eating disorders have a high risk of suicide, but in addition, the chronic malnutrition they suffer extracts a physical toll on the body.[28] The combined mental and physical assault boosts the mortality rate from death by

27 Eating Disorders on the College Campus. (2013). [ebook] National Eating Disorder Association, pp.5-35. Available at: https://www.nationaleatingdisorders.org/sites/default/files/CollegeSurvey/CollegiateSurveyProject.pdf [Accessed 12 Jan. 2019].

28 Fields, R. (2011). *The Deadliest Disorder.* [online] Psychology Today. Available at: https://www.psychologytoday.com/us/blog/the-new-brain/201103/the-deadliest-disorder-0 [Accessed 12 Jan. 2019].

sudden heart attack, multiple organ failure, and other deadly consequences of prolonged malnutrition. Making eating disorders the mental illness with the highest mortality rate. Knowing that makes early detection, intervention and treatment extremely important and gives an individual the best chance of recovery.

I was completely shocked when I discovered this. I remember depression and suicide being brought up when I was in grade school and college, but eating disorders were barely mentioned. And yet eating disorders, anorexia in particular, that have the highest mortality rate? Higher than depression! Woah.

Although picky eating is different from anorexia or bulimia and other eating disorders because it is phobia based instead of body image related, I think it is important to have a basic understanding of what a normal relationship with food should look like. "Normal" is different for everyone and a "normal" relationship with food is definitely not perfect.

If you've ever grown up with a friend or family member who has struggled with their own relationship with food, you understand that it isn't always as simple as it looks to have a "healthy" and "normal" diet because these words have so many different meanings attached to them by so many different people. This is important to keep this in mind with picky eaters as well. Parents are usually worried for their children's health and that their picky eaters aren't eating "normal" food. Normal is flexible and different for everyone. Your picky eater's diet is always going to be more "normal" then some and less "normal" than others and that is completely okay.

Picky Points:

- Remember food is not black or white, good or bad, healthy or unhealthy.
- Normal eating is different for everyone and is flexible.
- Eating disorders are the mental illness with the highest mortality rate.
- Be loving, patient, compassionate, understanding and hopeful with a picky eater or anyone struggling with their relationship with food.

CHAPTER 21

FOOD IS MEDICINE

———

"Your body wants to heal. It wants to be healthy. When you cut yourself, the wound heals. Food is medicine, and if you give your body what it needs, it will do what it can to heal."
~Stephanie Malsed

After twenty years as an interior designer Stephanie Malsed changed course and followed her passion for health and nutrition by becoming a Holistic Health Coach, Certified Nutrition Consultant, and Biofeedback Practitioner. She guides busy moms in gaining the knowledge and confidence in establishing healthy habits and raising the level of health and nutrition of their families. She's passionate about educating, empowering and inspiring families on their journey to living a life of abundance, happiness and health!

Back in 2008 was the beginning of Stephanie Malsed's healing journey, which has completely changed her approach to food.

When she was thirty-five, she suffered from a sacroiliac joint injury that left her with chronic pain night and day. After many months with no relief despite many medications and doctors, she took her chiropractor's advice and contacted a functional medicine practitioner. Functional medicine is a systems biology–based approach that focuses on identifying and addressing the root cause of disease. Each symptom or differential diagnosis may be one of many contributing to an individual's illness. Through various lab tests, she discovered that she had stage two adrenal fatigue, heavy metal toxicity, candida, impaired liver function, malabsorption and sensitivities to gluten and soy.

So she dove into the health and nutrition world further and decided to make significant lifestyle changes and overhaul her diet. She worked on healing her adrenals, detoxing heavy metals, cleansing her liver and doing exercises to correct posture and alignment imbalances. Her first step in changing her relationship with food was to eliminate gluten and soy from her diet. She was extremely resistant to this at first but couldn't deny that it had an immediate effect. She effortlessly dropped twenty-two pounds, had less bloating and gas, felt significantly better, and was finally able to heal her injury.

"This was my first glimpse into the profound effect food has on our bodies. After three years of diligent effort, I felt stronger and healthier than I had since high school," she offered.

**

But when Stephanie was first told ten years ago that she had to go gluten free and soy free, she freaked out. She thought, "What do you mean? What am I going to eat?"

She loves food and believes everything you eat should taste amazing. As she said, "If it doesn't, it's not worth eating." She didn't want to lose out on taste by going gluten and soy free. So she started on a learning path to create food that she could eat and that tasted good. This continues to be her inspiration after all these years.

She said, "Now I can eat gluten free and have all the taste and satisfaction that everyone else has as well."

Three years into living a gluten-free life, she was inspired to start a gluten-free cupcake business with her sister in Boulder, Colorado. Their goal was to create a gluten-free cupcake that no one knew was gluten free. She talked about how they made so many different batches of gluten-free cupcakes and were constantly bringing them over to their neighbor's house to test them. After lots and lots of taste testing, their neighbors finally said, "No more cupcakes!"

She's proud to say that all those test cupcakes paid off and they did it! They created a cupcake that was delicious and that their customers couldn't tell was gluten free. Stephanie and her sister went on to sell their successful cupcake business!

She has now chosen to be gluten free, soy free and alcohol free for over ten years and feels better than ever.

Stephanie says, "I think of it as a choice. I've chosen not to eat gluten and soy, and I've chosen not to drink. I've chosen to eat this way because I feel better and I want to let people know there are options and ways to feel better without missing out."

One of Stephanie's clients had extreme chronic adrenal fatigue for twenty years and was at the point where she could barely get out of bed in the morning. She'd start every day with two shots of espresso.

So Stephanie said, "Okay, let's start by adding in things that have lots of nutrients."

Her approach is to not tell her clients to stop doing this or that but instead starts with what to add in. The end goal is to replace the unhealthy habits with nutrient-rich foods that your body craves and becomes reliant on. You get to a point where you're not going to want or even need the unhealthy habits or food anymore.

Over the course of four months, on her own, without Stephanie's suggestion, her client was down to one or two shots of espresso a week instead of twice every morning because she was adding all these other great-nutritious foods into her diet. Once she started to feel better, she realized the shots of espresso were just crutches that she didn't need anymore.

Her client told her that every day she was feeling about 3 percent better and Stephanie was thrilled when one day her client said, "I now understand that food is medicine. I didn't really believe you before but now I do. I didn't realize how sick I was."

"Let thy food be thy medicine and thy medicine be thy food."
~Hippocrates (460-377 BC)

As Stephanie notes, "Our bodies really want to create homeostasis wherever we are, and it's not until we make those changes that we realize we really didn't feel very good before."

Stephanie says she believes the biggest challenge for people is overcoming the fear of "I'm going to miss out."

"Friends have flat out said to me I would love to eat healthier, but I'm afraid if I give up these things I'm not going to be able to do anything fun or eat out anymore."

For example, they worry that they would miss out on things like family picnics, taking the kids out to ice cream, dinner parties or going out for drinks. But you don't have to miss out on these experiences. You just have to learn how to navigate those situations. For example, Stephanie says, "If I'm going to a dinner party, I always bring a side or appetizer that I can eat as well. I'm not going to skip the occasion, but I'm going to make sure I'm covered so I'll bring something."

Another thing she's learned to do to navigate parties or events including alcohol is to ask for a seltzer water with a lemon or lime in it. "If you don't have something in your hand, everyone will ask you if you want a drink. They are nervous that you don't have something, so just get anything nonalcoholic to sip on and then enjoy the night." People will soon stop asking and won't worry about it anymore.

She said, "Sometimes, people will turn to me and say, 'I'm so sorry you can't have that,' when they see I'm not having a certain food or drink, and my response is usually, 'Oh I'm not. I feel great.'"

As the University of Minnesota says, "There are many reasons why we should pay attention to what we eat. The processed, low-variety foods many of us consume regularly may be convenient and tasty, but they compromise our health.

"We especially need to pay attention to what we eat when we are sick so we can give our bodies the nutrients they need to heal. And if you want to be even more deliberate in improving health—perhaps to address a chronic disease or condition—a Functional Medicine approach can yield great benefits.

"Overall, seeing your food as medicine helps you make better decisions about what (and how) to eat in order to make the best decisions for your own well-being."

When we consider the role food plays in our health with providing the nutrients our bodies need, we can't help but think about how the limited variety in food will affect a picky eater's health. But seeing food as medicine and crucial to our health is a bigger concern than just for picky eaters.

"As a society we are facing significant health problems:

- 78 percent of healthcare expenditures are for the treatment of chronic disease.

- Four of the top ten leading causes of death domestically are influenced by diet.
  1. heart disease
  2. cancer
  3. stroke
  4. diabetes
- Approximately 70 percent of the average American's diet consists of processed foods.
- In a recent USDA survey, 94 percent of schools served a lunch that failed to meet national standards for healthy school meals.

Many researchers now believe these problems are related to diet. While they used to believe that diseases—such as type II diabetes, obesity, heart disease, stroke, and certain cancers—were caused by a single gene mutation, they are now generally attributing these conditions to a network of biological dysfunction. And the food we eat is an important factor in that dysfunction, in part because our diets lack the necessary balance of nutrients. [29]

To prevent the onset of these diseases, we need to know how multiple nutrients in a diet interact and affect the human body's functions, according to the Nutrition Society, Europe's

29 Denton, C. (2016). *How Does Food Impact Health? | Taking Charge of Your Health & Wellbeing.* [online] Taking Charge of Your Health & Wellbeing. Available at: https://www.takingcharge.csh.umn.edu/ explore-healing-practices/food-medicine/how-does-food-impact-health [Accessed 12 Jan. 2019].

largest nutritional organization. Functional Medicine is a dynamic approach to assessing, preventing, and treating complex and chronic diseases using nutrition. This area of healthcare also conducts research on the role that nutrition plays in health.

The food we eat gives our bodies the nutrients and building blocks it needs to function properly. If we don't get the right nutrients, our metabolic processes suffer and our health declines.

If we get too much food, or food that gives our bodies the wrong instructions, we can become overweight, undernourished, and at risk for the development of diseases and conditions, such as arthritis, diabetes, and heart disease.

Stephanie adds, "It is also important to take into consideration bio-individuality. Each person has unique needs for his or her own health. According to Joshua Rosenthal, Founder and Director at the Institute for Integrative Nutrition, "One person's medicine may be another person's poison." Not only is the relationship to food important but connecting mindful observation to how the body is reacting is important to creating optimal health."

In short, what we eat is central to our health. There are thousands of articles about which foods provide the best support and nutrients for your body and to support your health. For now, though, here are fourteen superfoods I've noticed appear in article after article!

1. Avocados
2. Black Beans
3. Broccoli
4. Berries (blueberries especially)
5. Sweet Potatoes
6. Eggs
7. Spinach
8. Nuts (walnuts) (almonds)
9. Salmon
10. Kale
11. Oatmeal
12. Yogurt
13. Quinoa
14. Lentils

The year before I left for Belgium a large freckle appeared on my lip. This was a new freckle, not one that I had since I was little. The first few thoughts that ran through my head were, "What is that? Do I have skin cancer?" Naturally, I was concerned and I went to see the doctor. She told me we would have to take a biopsy, or a skin sample, where they remove skin cells to test for cancer. If you've ever had a biopsy, you'll know that it is not fun. Especially when they are cutting into really sensitive skin, such as your lip. It takes some time for the skin to heal back so I had a little scab on my lip that kept opening every time I'd eat.

Luckily, the results came back and the cells were not cancerous. It was just a sun spot, just a freckle, whew. I thought, "Thank goodness, it's nothing to worry about and now it's gone." I diligently took care of my lips and skin and the scab fully healed. Imagine my surprise when all of a sudden there appeared the freckle on my lip again. Strange. I asked my doctor if there was anything I could do about it. She said we could biopsy it again or leave it be and just be diligent with my sunscreen. I knew it wasn't cancerous so I wasn't too worried and figured I would just leave it be and have this freckle on my lip for the rest of my life. I packed up and moved to Belgium and didn't think too much of it after that.

Until after I started trying new foods. One day I did a double take when I looked at myself in the mirror and thought, "Hey, is my freckle smaller?" I couldn't quite tell and thought my eyes might be playing tricks on me. Next thing I knew, one day I looked in the mirror and it was just gone. I'm not exactly sure what nutrients my body was craving but something in my new diet made the freckle on my lip disappear. It was clear to me from that day forward that food is medicine and can heal us. Even if it is just a little freckle!

Picky Points:

- We are facing significant health problems as a nation that are related to diet.
- Food is medicine and can heal your body as well as treat and prevent disease.
- Our bodies need nutrients. Use nutritious food to support your immune system.

CHAPTER 22

EMOTIONAL FOOD

———

"For people to make a switch to eating healthier and making better choices about what they eat, they often need to overcome their deep-seated emotional patterns that come with food." ~Stephanie Malsed

There are a lot of different reasons for cravings and we all form patterns with eating from our family, society, and the media that influence what we eat. Stephanie admits that even she has experienced craving the emotional satisfaction from food to help cope with difficult situations.

In the fall of 2017 Stephanie went through an incredibly stressful situation that lasted seven months. The situation was largely out of her control, but she was regularly put in a position of proving her innocence over and over again.

During that time, all she wanted to do was eat was potato chips and chocolate. Over the winter every time she started stressing out about her situation, she'd turn to a bag of chips instead of going to yoga, or she'd grab that chocolate bar instead of going for a hike. This added up over seven months and resulted in her packing on an extra ten pounds.

She thought, "Well this is really interesting. Why am I doing this when I'm so cognizant of my health?"

Even though she knew intellectually that those foods were not good for her and that eating them would not benefit her, it was still extremely hard for her to overcome her ingrained emotional behaviors with food. At the end of that seven months, she was finally able to look at changing those patterns. She said, "Okay, I can't do this to my body anymore. I know what I need to do to regain my health and I need to do it."

She went to Costa Rica with her family in April 2017 and once she got back she was able to finally bring closure to the situation and move forward. She made a plan with a friend to start a thirty-day liver cleanse in the beginning of May. She was able to reset her diet, and guide him through the liver cleanse which not only helped him but also helped her stay accountable.

Now she can have a few potato chips without plowing through the whole bag and said, "For me, it's just being mindful. A lot of people don't think about their food choices. They just follow the pattern, and it's not until a situation arises where they have to make a change that they break the pattern."

There are really two components to this 1) addressing the stress or underlying emotion that is attached to the food and 2) addressing the food habit and craving that is in place. As a health coach, Stephanie makes sure to use a holistic approach with clients and is always considering stress levels and what can be done to help deal with them in a healthy way. For example, going for a walk, going to yoga, meditating, and just being honest with yourself about what's going on.

Stephanie says, "It's real and we just need to come up with ways to deal with it.

"Then you have to be very intentional with your choices so you don't just fall right back into those habits or patterns. You have to reset those patterns and replace them with healthier ones, not just ignore them or try to get rid of them."

Stephanie notes, "For a lot of people, that's a scary thought. What are they going to do if they can't go back to that pint of ice cream?

"Our brains have evolved to reward us with feelings of pleasure when we eat fat. We know exactly where in the brain this pleasure is felt—the lateral hypothalamus and amygdala. The higher the level of fat in a food the more active these parts of the brain become," according to the TV series, *Food: Delicious Science.*

Azriel ReShel covers it well in her article, "The Relationship between Food and Emotions."[30]

"Emotional eating is as mainstream as the iPhone. Sometimes we seem to be feeding our feelings rather than our bodies. Many human behaviors are driven by unconscious emotions.

"Psychological and physiological factors affect what we choose to put into our bodies and dictate the relationship we have between food and emotions. We need fuel in the form of food to survive, but there are absolutely some foods that are only eaten in very specific circumstances.

"One of the most popular foods people crave is chocolate. Chocolate contains a chemical called phenylethylamine, which is the same chemical our brain creates when we are feeling the emotion of romantic love.

---

30 ReShel, A. (2017). *The Relationship Between Food and Emotions.* [online] UPLIFT. Available at: https://upliftconnect.com/relationship-between-food-and-emotions/ [Accessed 12 Jan. 2019].

"We crave specific foods due to amino acids, neurochemical catalysts, or vasoconstrictor catalysts. These will energize your body or soothe your brain chemicals. If we take the example of someone experiencing fatigue or burnout, they may crave the stimulating effect of sharp cheese or red meat, or sugar and chocolate to give an instant energy hit. When people are depressed, fearful, or feeling lonely, they may start craving the soothing effect of fatty foods, like ice cream.

"Different foods satisfy our different emotional needs."

According to Healthline.com's article, "The 18 Most Addictive Foods," researchers at the University of Michigan studied addictive-like eating in 518 participants.[31] They used the Yale Food Addiction Scale (YFAS) as a reference. This is the most commonly used tool to assess food addiction.

All participants got a list of thirty-five foods, both processed and unprocessed. They rated how likely they were to experience problems with each of the thirty-five foods, on a scale from 1 (not at all addictive) to 7 (extremely addictive). In this study, 7–10 percent of participants were diagnosed with full-blown food addiction. What's more, **92 percent** of

---

31   Bjarnadottir, A. (2017). *The 18 Most Addictive Foods (and the 17 Least Addictive)*. [online] Healthline. Available at: https://www.healthline. com/nutrition/18-most-addictive-foods [Accessed 12 Jan. 2019].

participants had addictive-like eating behavior toward some foods. They repeatedly had the desire to quit eating them, but were unable to.

Not surprisingly, most of the foods rated as addictive were processed foods. These foods were usually high in sugar, fat or both. The number following each food is the average score given in the study mentioned above, on a scale from 1 (not at all addictive) to 7 (extremely addictive). Here are the top eighteen most addictive foods:

1. Pizza (4.01)
2. Chocolate (3.73)
3. Chips (3.73)
4. Cookies (3.71)
5. Ice cream (3.68)
6. French fries (3.60)
7. Cheeseburgers (3.51)
8. Soda (not diet) (3.29)
9. Cake (3.26)
10. Cheese (3.22)
11. Bacon (3.03)
12. Fried chicken (2.97)
13. Rolls (plain) (2.73)
14. Popcorn (buttered) (2.64)
15. Breakfast cereal (2.59)
16. Gummy candy (2.57)

17. Steak (2.54)

18. Muffins (2.50)

Psychotherapist and spiritual teacher, Doreen Virtue, the author of *Constant Cravings,* says, "Cravings for food are a sign that the body and the emotions are looking for peace or homeostasis. They can stem from emotional or physical imbalances."

She continues, "There can be a physical basis for food cravings. If you are missing out on minerals or vitamins, or have an imbalance in your diet, you will crave certain foods. Once you've fixed the physical aspects of your food cravings, what is left are the emotional causes. If your emotional issues remain unaddressed, your food craving will remain constant. If your emotional issues change, so will your food cravings."

"If your cravings seem more geared toward high fat foods, you're most likely feeling some insecurity that you're trying to fill with fat. Fat stays in the stomach long after other forms of food have been digested and emptied. So, fat cravings often occur in people who feel that their life lacks meaning, who feel empty, or who feel financially or emotionally insecure.

"The most direct route to reducing cravings is to heal the situation that's triggering them. Even taking a baby step toward the resolution of a problem at work, in your love life, or in your lifestyle can reduce food cravings.

"While our moods impact our diet, conversely our diet impacts our emotions and state of mind. Ultimately, it can be a vicious circle.

"Food cravings are most often an emotional hunger. They're your body's way of communicating a basic need that's not being met. Perhaps it's a need for comfort, touch, love, support, validation, or connection. By listening to yourself and uncovering what you are needing and then filling these emotions yourself, or reaching out to a friend for support, you can start to nourish yourself emotionally. You'll soon find your food cravings will drop off.

"Our body is naturally wired for optimum health and balance. We become thirsty when we are dehydrated, we shiver when we are cold, and yawn when tired. These are the body's messages for us to take action to meet our needs. In the same way, when we lose our peace of mind, our body directs us with an action to correct it. It could deliver a food craving for chocolate, which is really a way of saying you need to correct your emotional state of mind, which is feeling lonely, anxious or insecure.

"If we can learn the difference between emotional and physical hunger, we can easily meet our emotional needs and stave off cravings. Some differences between these two types of hunger are:

1. Emotional hunger is based in the mind, is sudden and specific, wanting one food.
2. Physical hunger comes from the stomach, is slower and is open to a variety of foods.

"Ultimately, we need to face our emotions instead of covering them up with food. While this may seem scary or challenging, it is the pathway to radiant health and vitality, along with balance and happiness. When our body is well nourished and healthy our emotions become calmer, and the mind happier and more balanced, so it's a journey well worth taking."[32]

I wish when I was younger either I had noticed or someone had identified that I was feeling fear every time I was presented with a new food to try. It is clear to me now but at the time I couldn't identify that anxiety and fear were the symptoms and emotions I was experiencing. It never occured to me to connect my extremely picky eating with an emotion. I am so grateful for this knowledge now. We relate so

---

32 ReShel, A. (2017). *The Relationship Between Food and Emotions.* [online] UPLIFT. Available at: https://upliftconnect.com/relationship-between-food-and-emotions/ [Accessed 12 Jan. 2019].

many different emotions to food and when fear is involved, extremely picky eaters with SED are formed.

Our emotions are tied to the food we eat both for our benefit and to our detriment. We can't help it. It is how we are programmed. It is natural. Use this knowledge to your benefit and start paying attention to what your body is trying to tell you.

Picky Points:

- Our emotions are tied to the food we eat. Food cravings are driven by our subconscious emotions.
- Emotional hunger is based in the mind, is sudden and specific, wanting one food.
- Physical hunger is based in the stomach, is slower, and open to a variety of foods.
- Ask yourself where you may be using food in your life to address stress or a certain difficult emotion.

CHAPTER 23

FOOD BELIEFS

——

"I know those early experiences with food affect us." ~Kay (Her struggles with wanting to represent her family well are still so strong that she has asked that I only use her common first name.)

Kay grew up in a household where her mom and her sister struggled with eating disorders. She would see her mom or her sister eat something they thought they shouldn't eat and break down afterward from feelings of enormous shame, isolation, anger and self-hate.

This meant from an early age she learned there was a precise list of what should be eaten and what should not be eaten. Everything not on the list would result in a very unpleasant experience—even "dangerous." What she meant by that is how unsettling and upsetting it could be at times to not know if the grown-ups around her would be able to take care of her. The binges they had were often referred to as "eating attacks." It did feel at times to her as if there was a monster at the door.

She said, "There was no sense of safety around food. It was such a sad thing to learn. I mean you can't go without food for your whole life, not even for a few days. So every time you 'had' to eat, it felt like you were taking out a stick of dynamite.

"When my mom started binging, her mood would change and it was similar to being a child of an alcoholic. I felt like I was constantly trying to gauge what mood my mom was in that day."

There is a lot of pressure on children to look, act and, yes, even eat, a certain way. Kay felt a lot of pressure to be the thin one in her family. Her body was sort of the proof her family would push out in front of everyone to show, "See, we are okay because this child looks how society thinks she should look."

Kay struggled with her own relationship with food in college after watching her mother and sister binge growing up. She has been vegetarian, vegan, a natural biotic and gone through several other versions of selective diets.

At one point while she was in grad school, she decided she wanted to try and add some protein to her diet. She decided on tuna out of a can because it was so convenient, but she had to figure out a way to justify adding this to her list of okay foods and she told me, "It's funny. I thought, 'Okay in the *Bible* we have Jesus with the fish, so it must be okay to eat fish,' and I was able to justify that I could start eating not only tuna but also salmon." She was then able to make this small change and add some protein into her diet.

When Kay was twenty-three years old, she was really stressed out at work and had just come down with mononucleosis (mono). Mono is a virus with symptoms including fatigue, sore throat, fever, swollen lymph nodes or tonsils, headaches and a rash. She was completely exhausted. Her mom had heard about a new center and so she convinced Kay to go. When Kay got there, she realized that almost everyone else there was much older than she was and had one kind of chronic medical condition or another. She remembers going to these lectures that they would have at night where they would hold up an egg and then proceed to describe it as this evil thing full of bad cholesterol. Another lecture described eating meat as similar to eating a Lego if you haven't eaten it in a while. As Kay said, "This stuff really gets in your head."

And our health is not just affected by the nutrients we put into our body. It is also uniquely impacted by our mind. Our individual thoughts and our beliefs about food are as different and unique as each of us. If you truly believe that an egg is the worst thing in the world for you, and then you eat an egg, you are going against your own subconscious beliefs and your body will rebel. If you believe that an egg is really healthy for you with lots of nutritious benefits, you will happily eat an egg without worrying about it. It will benefit you all the more.

As the James Beard Foundation contributor, Miriam Around, said in her article *The Power of Food: Belief vs. Reality,* "While our study suggests that we've reached a tipping point, with Americans now recognizing that eating healthfully is key to their body and mind, there's still a disparity between what they believe and how they act. Yes, they've taken steps to eat more consciously: 72% say they eat more fruits and vegetables and 44% are more likely than in the past to choose whole grains over refined ones. But more than half of our respondents--61%--say they don't eat healthfully--and almost all (90%) wish their diet was healthier than it is. They don't blame their less-than-ideal eating patterns on not being able to find healthy food in supermarkets or on a lack of government interventions. Instead, the biggest health hurdles they cite are: money (four out of five think healthy food is more expensive); taste (half of them like junk food better); and lack of time (half of them think healthy food takes more time to prepare).

"As a magazine that speaks to more than 17 million Americans each month (and an additional 9 million on our website), our mission at Good Housekeeping is to show people how eating healthfully can be affordable, easy, realistic, and delicious. But for massive behavioral changes to take place, we all need to step up to the proverbial plate. There's a huge opportunity for health practitioners to provide patients with guidelines and resources for eating better. But a study released this past June showed that 75% of doctors feel they receive inadequate training to effectively counsel their patients about diet. It also noted that fewer than 30% of medical schools meet the minimum number of recommended education hours in nutrition and exercise science. The gap between the public's readiness to learn more about how to eat well and the medical profession's lack of acceptance of this responsibility is almost as though, years ago, the public had understood that seat belts could be life saving but cars didn't come equipped with them. Americans need more medical practices to have registered dieticians on board, schools that educate about simple ways to eat nutritiously, packaged food companies to develop ingredient-conscious products, and restaurants to serve tempting and delicious healthy recipes."[33]

It is possible to have a healthy diet that is affordable.

---

33   Arond, M. (2014). *The Power of Food: Belief vs. Reality.* [online] Huff-Post. Available at: https://www.huffpost.com/entry/the-power-of-food-belief_b_6037176 [Accessed 15 Jan. 2019].

It is possible to have a healthy diet that is easy.

It is possible to have a healthy diet that tastes good.

It is possible to have a healthy diet that doesn't take a long time to prepare.

Healthy is possible and much more attainable than you probably believe right now.

It is important to be careful and try not to transfer your potentially harmful beliefs about food to your children. The best thing you can do instead is to figure out what your food beliefs are and change the beliefs that are not benefiting you.

When I was young, I created a subconscious belief that new food was dangerous. I don't know exactly when or how this happened but it did. This subconscious belief then created a fear, or phobia, of new food to try and protect me from what I subconsciously believed was dangerous. Thus I became an extremely picky eater with a limited diet of foods "I," or my subconscious, had decided were "safe." This belief would stay with me for over 29 years of my life. Felix Economkis was able to identify this subconscious belief and bring my conscious awareness to it. To show the conscious "me" that this belief was not benefiting me and was, in fact, harming me. This awareness was crucial in overcoming my phobia of food and giving me the ability to try new foods.

Your mind is a powerful tool and when used correctly can be a force of nature. When you understand the role your conscious and subconscious mind and beliefs play in your health and body and learn how to tap into that, you can do anything.

Picky Points:

- Our subconscious beliefs play a critical role in our health.
- Healthy is possible, is affordable, is easy, tastes good, and doesn't have to take a lot of time.
- Evaluate your food beliefs and how they may be impacting your health.

RECIPE

BAKED POTATO

—

Next is a baked potato and we are back to cooking in the oven. With a baked potato we really are focusing on the change in texture. Although a baked potato and french fries are both potatoes the textures of these two sides are very different. A lot of extremely picky eaters love french fries but won't eat a baked potato. There needs to be a few smaller changes in texture before jumping between these two. With a baked potato you lose almost all of the crispy, crunchy texture and are really focused on the potato taste itself with a much softer texture. You can also try a hasselback baked potato to keep a little bit more of the crispy edges in while experiencing the softer baked potato texture as well.

INGREDIENTS

- 4 Russet Potatoes
- 1/4 cup Olive Oil
- Butter
- Salt
- Pepper

INSTRUCTIONS

1. Heat the oven to 425°F.
2. Wash and dry the potatoes.
3. Pierce each potato 2–3 times with a fork.
4. Rub oil all over the potatoes.
5. Rub salt all over the potatoes.
6. Place the potatoes on a baking sheet and bake for 45 minutes to an hour. The exact baking time will depend on how large the potatoes are. The potato should be tender inside if you poke a fork into it.
7. Serve with butter, salt, pepper, cheese, chives, sour cream and all of your favorite toppings!

FOR A FUN TWIST ON A BAKED POTATO, ADD A FEW ADDITIONAL STEPS AND TRY A HASSELBACK BAKED POTATO.

INSTRUCTIONS

1. Heat the oven to 425°F with a rack in the lower-middle position.
2. Wash and dry the potatoes.

3. Cut slits into the potato, stopping just before you cut through so that the slices stay connected at the bottom of the potato. Space the slices 1/8-inch to 1/4-inch apart. You can rest the potato in a large serving spoon and use that as a guide for when to stop slicing. Slice straight down and when your knife hits the edge of the spoon, stop slicing.

4. Brush the potatoes with olive oil.

5. Sprinkle with salt and pepper.

6. Bake 30 minutes, then nudge layers apart and brush with butter.

7. Bake another 30 to 40 minutes until the potatoes are crispy on the edges and easily pierced in the middles with a paring knife.

8. If you're adding any extras, (cheese, sour cream, bacon, minced herbs) stuff those into the slits and sprinkle over the top 5 to 10 minutes before the end of cooking.

9. Serve immediately: These potatoes are best straight from the oven while the edges are at their crispiest.

10. Add a little salt on top when you take them out.

PART 6

WHAT NOT TO DO

Earlier we talked a little bit about what to do to support and encourage a picky eater. Now we are going to dive into what not to do. There are several common mistakes, misunderstandings, and misconceptions currently being suggested out there that simply do not help the picky eater in your life and, in some cases, can even make things worse. In this section we talk a little bit about blame and shame, the detriments of forcing food, why we should be wary of the American diet mindset, and current notions about the health of a picky eater.

CHAPTER 24

DON'T BLAME YOURSELF OR OTHERS

———

Food shouldn't be scary, right? It should be exciting, delicious and nutritious. But what happens when food, the thing we rely upon to survive, is your greatest fear? When the one thing you must have every day is the last thing you want to have?

As I mentioned previously, Thanksgiving was always one of the most conflicted days of the year for me. When November rolled around each year, everyone was excited about all the food—the turkey, the homemade gravy, and of course our three different types of stuffing—and I knew I'd be having the same grilled cheese or PB&J sandwich I had for dinner every other day of the year.

Talk about feeling different and humiliated. Especially when there were young children around who could eat more food than me. For the most part, friends and family would try to be accommodating and weren't trying to humiliate me or make me feel different. Although that did sometimes happen too, and I just couldn't help feeling ashamed with the casual side eyes toward my plate and little comments like, "You're missing out," and "Stuffing is the BEST. You really should try it. It just tastes like bread."

A lot of self-shaming happened. You couldn't ask me a question that I hadn't already asked myself or been asked by others over and over again:

- What's wrong with you?
- Why can't you be normal and just try it?
- Why don't you just take one bite?
- It's not going to kill you. It won't hurt you. Just eat it.
- What's the worst that will happen? You'll just throw it back up or spit it out.

or

- Just try it. It hardly tastes like anything.
- Aren't you going to eat anything?
- Is that all you're having?
- Aren't you hungry?

- What do you actually eat? What about... (fill in the blank)?
- How do you survive off of that?
- Are you vegetarian or vegan? Is there something else I can get you?

People are curious. That's just how we are. When people ask, "Why aren't you eating this?" and "Why don't you just try it?" they are just being normal, curious people. It is our natural instinct to want to know why someone is doing something different. Even after being a picky eater my entire life, I too will naturally wonder when someone orders something different or has a special order. Partly because I wonder if they are also an extremely picky eater and partly because I have that same curiosity that pops into my head.

Most people actually want to help and see if they can come up with something to offer you. Though at the time, it doesn't always feel that way. You want it to be a nonissue, not talked about, not worried about and just left alone. When they are really trying to come up with something for you to eat, it can feel like it is bringing so much more attention and embarrassment to the one thing you don't want to discuss although they are really just trying to help.

Sometimes though you also have people who aren't well-intentioned and are simply mean who make fun of you, embarrass you, and laugh at you. Others will just blame you and those around you. I can't even count the number of times I heard my parents being blamed for my picky eating with a comment such as, "I'd never let my child get away with that" or "My parents never would let me have a diet like that."

I hated that my parents were blamed. I wasn't trying to make things more difficult for them or make them look like bad parents. That's not what I wanted. I blamed myself for making all of our lives more difficult than they could have been. Even well-intentioned friends and family who loved us would sometimes do more harm than good with their criticisms and comments that, "You're just being too easy on her and not strict enough."

Felix Economakis says it well,

"Parents can't win with this one. Either they are blamed for having been too soft or too hard, or too absent or too interfering. Countless clients have told me that once they started seeing therapists about their food phobias, the therapists start asking the client about the relationship with their mother. While it is certainly true that in a relatively small minority of cases, the family dynamics led to issues of control around food, in the vast majority of cases it does not. In which case, not only is it unjust to blame the parents but it is also insulting.

"To put this in perspective, last year I got sick and later on that night I threw up a few times. As it happens, my last meal was spaghetti with a tomato sauce, one of my favorites. For about a week after, I lost all interest in one of my favorite meals. My defense system played it safe by developing a temporary aversion to pasta. Because I am an adult and a psychologist and I can 'reason' with myself, and the aversion was short lived. However, now imagine that instead of this event happening at my current age, instead it happened at the age of two years old. My defense system would have exaggerated the nature of the scare and potentially put me off all pasta, or even all pasta-like foods.

"Remember that scares are a much bigger deal when we are younger. A medium-sized dog barking at me at my current age is no big deal. I tower over the dog, and I don't feel threatened. The same dog suddenly barking at me as a two-year-old is the equivalent size of a tiger. It is a bigger deal to the 'me' of that time.

"One mother of a child with SED told me that she was a nutritionist and dietician. She told me, 'Trust me. If anyone knew about a healthy diet, it was me,' but still her child could not eat the various foods she prepared. Another very common comment is that if SED is related to the quality of parenting around food, when all things are equal, it would stand to reason that all the other siblings would develop the same problems around food. As one client of mine mentioned: 'My brothers (three of them) all eat normally. We were all raised together and I'm the middle child. My parents did nothing differently with food when we were born. One difference was that I had severe colic as a newborn.' Colic (or early association of pain with feeding) is a major source of SED.

"To conclude on this point, you could be 'mother of the year' and still not make a dent in SED because the phobic response has its own circuit that will run regardless of your parenting. In the meantime, it is very difficult being judged by others for something you are innocent of. Always assuming it is the parents' fault is another inaccurate myth that needs to be re-evaluated in the cold light of evidence."

I am lucky. I have an extremely supportive family and I have wonderful friends. My family would always do what they could to make me feel included. My mom and dad would help me make my cheese quesadilla or grilled cheese and my sisters would tell me not to worry about it. They would reassure me that, "There are people being picky about their menu choices at restaurants every day. It's no big deal."

My friends and family would make sure we went to restaurants where they knew there was something on the menu I could eat. They would encourage me to go out to dinner and we always had fun. They would stick up for me with the waiters and waitresses, and my friends got used to me just eating the bread or ordering some french fries. I always did my best to not let my picky eating detract from my social life. I'm a social person and love spending time with my friends and family at restaurants, parties and events (although it wasn't always easy).

For years, my mom would say how all she wanted for Christmas would be for me to try new foods. Although with the very best of intentions, this also felt like a lot of pressure. That's the one thing I couldn't give her and it's all she wanted! For me to be okay and normal and healthy and eat like everyone else. The thing is I really, really wanted that too!

You can imagine when FINALLY for the first time in my entire life I was able to eat Thanksgiving and Christmas dinner with my family and eat ALL of the food that was being served in 2017. It was literally a dream come true for me! I could not only enjoy the social aspect of Thanksgiving but could finally understand what it was like to both look forward to and enjoy the food as well.

I tried all of the appetizers, not just the cheese and crackers but the salami too, deviled eggs, shrimp with cocktail sauce, pineapple, strawberries, melon, carrots and celery with blue cheese, the spinach and artichoke dip, salmon and pork roulette, and even our family recipes for cardones and clams casino. At dinner I wasn't passing everything along as quickly as possible but actually putting all of it on my plate as well! It was amazing! I ate turkey and gravy, tried both the dry and wet stuffing, squash, corn, broccoli and cauliflower, cranberry sauce and mashed potatoes!

Picky Points:

- Don't blame yourself or others for your picky eating.
- Don't be ashamed. It isn't your fault.
- Don't judge picky eater parents. It's not their fault either.
- People are naturally curious and will ask questions (most often) to try and help.

CHAPTER 25

DON'T FORCE IT

—

Every time I was told, "If you don't eat this dinner with us, you won't eat," I'd just go to bed without eating or I'd sneak off and steal Pop-Tarts from the pantry and hide them in my room to eat later.

One night when I was eight years old, after continuous pressure from family and friends, my parents sat me down at the head of our kitchen table with a little clear glass dish in front of me with plain spaghetti with a light butter sauce and stated I wasn't leaving the table until I at least tried it, and I wasn't having anything else for dinner. I remember sitting there and crying and crying and screaming at them and telling them how horrible and mean they were to do this to me. I wanted to eat the stupid pasta but I just couldn't. It felt like they were asking me to eat this little dish of disgusting worms and I would choke and die if I tried. I went to bed hungry and everyone went to bed unhappy and miserable. My parents were doing their best with what they had been told to do to get me to try new foods, but what wound up happening was I developed an even deeper aversion and fear of pasta. Later on it took me longer to get used to pasta than some of the other new foods I tried.

Unfortunately, this does not help picky eaters with trying new foods. All it does is put a strain on the relationship between the picky eater and their parents. So let's leave the "You can't leave the table until you try it" behind.

When my parents tried sneaking something in my food, all it did was create mistrust. I'd usually figure it out pretty quickly and then I'd be even more mistrustful of unfamiliar food or even familiar foods being prepared by other people. This was definitely not the intended outcome they were hoping for and, unfortunately, it only made things worse. Trust me that is not what you want.

As Felix puts it, "Another big myth about picky eaters is the notion that if you are truly starving, you will end up eating anything because of your body's overriding instinct for self-preservation. Yes, many people in emergency situations have ended up eating things they wouldn't normally consider eating! Despite this, however, this is another myth that is easily debunked with numerous examples to the contrary.

"With a little bit of analysis, the same people who believe this myth are at a loss to explain:

- The existence of anorexia. Many thousands of people with anorexia have successfully starved themselves to death, overriding any instinct of self-preservation. In one sense, a person with anorexia has a phobia of being fat rather than a phobia of certain foods. In either case, the body is able to prevent consumption of much needed food.
- Hunger strikes. One may argue that people with anorexia have a mental disorder, which influences their judgement, so they do not count. Be that as it may, what about hunger strikes which are usually motivated for political reasons? Many people on hunger strikes have succeeded in starving themselves to death.

Putting aside food for the moment, evidence tells us countless people have been able to override any instinct for self-preservation with any number of self-inflicted deaths. Leaving aside the whole matter of 'conventional' suicides (such as people who commit suicide after a relationship breakdown), what about people who have even been prepared to set themselves on fire in protest at some action? If a person is prepared to suffer the excruciating pain of burning themselves to death all in order to merely make a statement they believe in, clearly the instinct for self-preservation is not the "be-all-and-end-all."

Let's flip to the other side of that coin—overeating. According to Peter Menzel, "Here in the United States we are the world leaders in eating ourselves to death," or as Michael Pollan said it, "Americans are getting fatter and its killing us."

According to Michael Pollan, "Three of every five Americans are overweight, one of every five is obese. 17 percent of kids age six through nineteen are obese. This is a giant public health problem costing the healthcare system an estimated $90 billion a year."

One way we can help decrease the chance of obesity in children is by saying goodbye to the "Clean Your Plate Club." Don't force your child to clean their plate before leaving the table. Unfortunately, the practice of forcing children to "clean their plates" can encourage them to develop bad eating habits, such as eating when they're not hungry. It can also lead to a distaste for those nutritious foods they're being forced to eat. It teaches children to ignore their body and hunger cues instead of learning how to listen to their bodies and identify when they're hungry and when they're full.

A 2007 study published in *Appetite* revealed that 85 percent of parents use praise, food rewards, and reasoning to get young children to eat more during mealtime. Another study published in *Pediatrics* showed that more than half of parents expect their adolescent children to clean their plates. A third prompted their children to eat more, even after declaring they were full. In 2008, Brian Wansink, author of "Mindless Eating," found that boys who were required to clean their plates at home asked for large portions of food outside the home.[34]

Don't bribe your child or use a reward-based approach. It's common for parents to offer a "special"—and often unhealthy—food as a reward for good behavior or a job well done. They may also withhold those special treats as a means of punishment. How many times have we heard, "If you finish your plate, you can have a dessert," or "You can't have a cookie until you finish cleaning your room?"

Although well intentioned to try and get your child to eat the rest of their vegetables or clean their room, this usually has unintended consequences. The child is learning that desserts have a higher value and are worth more than vegetables. They are learning to reward themselves with food.

---

34 Weiss, L. (2013). *Nutrition expert: Kids shouldn't be forced to clean their plates.* [online] Digitaljournal.com. Available at: http://www.digitaljournal.com/article/355871#ixzz5bmcSxUNr [Accessed 12 Jan. 2019].

According to the University of Rochester Medical Center, "Using food as a reward or as a punishment can undermine the healthy eating habits that you're trying to teach your children. Giving sweets, chips, or soda as a reward often leads to children overeating foods that are high in sugar, fat, and empty calories. Worse, it interferes with kids' natural ability to regulate their eating. It also encourages them to eat when they're not hungry to reward themselves."[35]

It's also confusing. We are told we should enjoy and eat foods with lots of nutrients that are healthy for us and avoid foods that are processed with little nutritional value. But then when kids are told they can indulge in foods that are "bad" for them as a reward for doing something good, we are sending a mixed message. They might even associate "unhealthy" foods with a certain mood or feeling such as when you feel good about yourself, it's okay to reach for a sweet or dessert. When sweets or chips are given as a reward, they may become more appealing and when healthier food must be finished, it becomes less appealing.

Major health organizations like the American Academy of Pediatrics recommend the Satter Division of Responsibility

35   Adler, L. and Bass, P. (2019). *Why Parents Shouldn't Use Food as Reward or Punishment - Health Encyclopedia - University of Rochester Medical Center.* [online] Urmc.rochester.edu. Available at: https://www.urmc.rochester.edu/encyclopedia/content.aspx?ContentType-ID=160&ContentID=32 [Accessed 12 Jan. 2019].

of feeding. That means parents decide the *what, when* and *where* of feeding and children decide the *how much* and *whether* of eating. This not only helps children self-regulate and build confidence in their eating. It makes mealtime more peaceful and supportive, so children can move along food acceptance at their own pace.

Picky Points:

- Forcing your picky eater to try something doesn't work. It deepens their fear.
- Tricking your picky eater into trying something doesn't work. It creates mistrust.
- Starving your picky eater doesn't work. Just because they are hungry does not mean they will eat it.
- Encourage your child to tune in to when they are hungry and full. Don't force them to clean their plate.
- Don't use food as a reward or punishment.

CHAPTER 26

DON'T FALL FOR THE DIET MINDSET

———

"Our current diet culture in the United States has stemmed from the belief that we don't know how to eat and we can't trust our bodies." ~Virginia Sole Smith

So many adults don't trust themselves around food. They've probably been dieting for years and don't know what to believe anymore. The messages around food we receive in our culture are so conflicting and confusing.

As Michael Pollan says, "We have no food culture in America, so every question about eating is up for grabs: fats or carbs, three meals a day or little snacks all day, raw or cooked, organic or industrial, vegetarian or omnivore?"

Gluten-free diets, no sugar diets, and no carb diets have all been prevalent recently, which leads to people feeling tons of guilt around foods like bread and pasta. However, kids are naturally drawn to these types of food when they are young and establishing their eating habits. Try to steer clear of strict diets where there are harsh rules about what you can and cannot eat.

Virginia said, "At my daughter's birthday party, I was cutting up a birthday cake and one of the little girls said to me, 'It's not good to eat cake every day.' I was shocked to hear this from a little girl who was so young. And yet, how often do you hear moms say, 'I can't lose the baby weight' or 'I shouldn't be eating this cheese' or 'I can't have sugar.' We berate ourselves constantly around food and that can be a confusing message for a child especially for one who is picky."

Virginia mentioned, "The other week I was at a restaurant waiting in line for the bathroom and there was an older, moderately sized woman standing next to me in line. Two women walked past us who were overweight and the woman next to me turned and said, "Wow sometimes it's really good for me to see that to remind me that at least I'm not that bad." I simply said to her, "Well we all come in different shapes and sizes."

Virginia said, "One of our biggest challenges is that we have outsourced our expertise on eating. We think we need to turn to these diet plans and gurus to tell us what to eat instead of being able to trust our own bodies and hunger."

It's difficult to figure out what would be the best for your health and diet.

One person says eggs are bad for you,
...another says meat is bad for you,
...another says sugar is bad for you,
...another says bread is bad for you,
...another says salt is bad for you,
...another says dairy is bad for you,
...another says gluten is bad for you,
...another says butter is bad for you.

It's very confusing and overwhelming.

All these rules about what is and isn't good or bad for you. When did eating become so complicated?

Instead of worrying about all these "diets" and things we should or shouldn't have, I think it's important to take a look at what nutritionists, doctors, and health experts from all over the world agree upon.

This is what I've found to be universally true. When you look at all of the published nutrition textbooks in the United States and countries all over the world, this is the consistent advice I found helpful to follow:

- Eat lots of vegetables. They have lots of nutrients.
- Eat lots of fruits. They have lots of nutrients.
- Drink lots of water.
- Eat when you are hungry to sustain a healthy weight.
- Eat until you are mostly full (not stuffed) to sustain a healthy weight.
- Eat and drink in moderation.
- Eat a variety of different foods for balanced health.
- Eat real food, not processed food.
- Trust your body and how you feel after eating something.

I've seen the examples for why to include or exclude so many different things from your diet, and I've also seen numerous exceptions. And there are exceptions for every single "rule" "diet" "bad food" and "good food" out there. This has led me to believe one thing—every person's diet and health is unique. There is not a one size fits all diet. Try to be understanding and flexible with yourself and enjoy your food and eating. You are better off with a couple of potato chips every now and then while mostly eating real foods than saying absolutely no potato chips and then (when you inevitably break your rule) eating a whole bag of them in one sitting.

Virginia says, "What we should do about it is tricky because getting back to a place where you can trust yourself around food is really hard for a lot of people. One small thing I do is I never talk negatively about my body in front of my daughter and I never talk bad about food in front of others. If a guest makes a comment about eating no bad foods, I'll say, 'We don't food shame in my house' so at least my daughter is hearing me cutting it down. You know what your body needs and I really try to emphasize that. It's hard though and I haven't always been able to catch it or say something right in the moment. I often feel like I'm a buzzkill if my friend says, 'Oh I really shouldn't eat this cheese' and I say something like, 'Oh I love cheese!' Unfortunately, food shaming in our culture can be a way of bonding."

According to Michael Pollan, "It boils down to this: as creatures who can eat many different things, how do we know what's good to eat and what's not—that's the omnivore's dilemma and it's growing bigger every day. There are lots of countries where people solve the omnivore's dilemma the old fashioned way. They eat traditional foods following customs that haven't changed for hundreds of years and amazingly, in those countries that eat food based on custom and taste, the people are actually healthier than we are in America.

"They have lower rates of diet-related illnesses such as heart disease. Take the French for example. They eat by and large the same way they have eaten for generations. They drink wine, eat cheese, cook with butter, eat red meat and eat bread without worrying about it, yet their rates of heart disease and obesity are lower than Americans.

"Maybe it is because HOW we eat is just as important as WHAT we eat. French culture includes a set of customs or rules about how they eat. For example, the French eat small portions and don't go back for seconds. They don't snack. They don't eat while driving or walking down the street. They seldom eat alone, instead eating with family or friends, and the meals are long leisurely affairs. The French culture of food allows the French to enjoy their food and be healthy at the same time."

When it comes to your health, so many other factors come into play in addition to how we eat: diet, exercise, genetics, your family, your community, your job and sense of purpose. Our bodies ARE all shaped differently and we all process food differently, so there are differences in what I need compared to what someone else might need.

"Most people who live to old age do so, not because they have beaten cancer, heart disease, depression or diabetes. Instead, the long-lived avoid serious ailments altogether through a series of steps that often rely on long-lasting, meaningful connections with others," says University of California,

Riverside, psychologist Howard S. Friedman, PhD, co-author with Leslie Martin, PhD, of the 2011 book *The Longevity Project*.[36]

The *The Longevity Project* is a compilation of findings from their work on an eight-decade research project of the same name examining the longevity of more than 1,500 children first studied by psychologist Lewis Terman, PhD, in 1921. It's an attempt to answer the question of who lives longest—and why—based on personality traits, relationships, experiences and career paths.

The Terman sample is the only lifelong, continuously detailed, large-scale study of initially healthy boys and girls. Because they had access to and understanding of medical care and education, but have a great range of personalities and social relations, it was a terrific sample for studying individual differences. Other studies document the health relevance of socioeconomic status, ethnicity and general intelligence, but *The Longevity Project* yields deep biopsychosocial insight into those macro-level associations.

---

36 Friedman, H. and Martin, L. (2012). The Longevity Project: Surprising Discoveries for Health and Long Life from the Landmark Eight-Decade Study. *Population and Development Review*, 38(1), pp.175-176.

Friedman and Martin said, "We were amazed to uncover lots of evidence overall that it is not random who will become ill. Rather, there are large differences in susceptibility to injury and disease. Some of these are a function of personality. Others are tied to social relations, including marriage, family, friendships and religious observance. Most eye-opening is our finding that the risk factors and protective shields do not occur in isolation, but bunch together in patterns.[37]

"For example, the unconscientious boys—even though very bright—were more likely to grow up to have poor marriages, to smoke and drink more, achieve less education, and be relatively unsuccessful at work. They died at younger ages. Such health risks and relationship challenges, such as divorce, are usually studied independently, which I think is a big mistake.

"Conversely, certain personality constellations predicted more achievement, better social relationships, stable families and other elements of thriving that led to longer, healthier lives. An individual with better health and longer life is the conscientious sort, with good friends, meaningful work and a happy, responsible marriage. They are thoughtful, prudent, and persistent achievers who invest in their careers and their

---

37 Novotney, A. (2011). *The real secrets to a longer life*. [online] http://www.apa.org. Available at: https://www.apa.org/monitor/2011/12/longer-life.aspx [Accessed 12 Jan. 2019].

relationships, which promotes long life naturally and automatically, even when challenges arise."[38]

It is clear that when it comes to living for a long time, your diet is not the only factor. There are so many other components that come into play with our health including your personality, your relationships and meaningful connections with others. But with our health we aren't only striving for long life. Yes, we want to live for a long time. But what are the other things we want when we say we want to be healthy? What are we trying to achieve with our diet and our health? Why do you want to go on a diet? Why do you want to change your health? The real question is: Why? Spend some time really diving into this question.

Do you want to live longer so you can spend more time with your family? Do you want to lose weight to be more desirable? To minimize disease? To feel better about yourself? To have more energy? To be able to concentrate better? To be sleep better? To be stronger? To achieve your goals?

Often what we are striving for is to be happy. Keep that in mind when you are deciding what to eat. Don't fall for a diet

---

38 NPR.org. (2011). *Secrets To Longevity: It's Not All About Broccoli.* [online] Available at: https://www.npr.org/2011/03/24/134827587/ secrets-to-longevity-its-not-all-about-broccoli [Accessed 12 Jan. 2019].

mindset that makes you unhappy. Food can be nutritious, life supporting and also enjoyable. Align what you eat to support your life and your body in the best way possible.

Picky Points:

- Learn to trust your body and yourself with food.
- Don't food shame yourself or others.
- Don't fall for the diet mindset.
- How we eat is just as important as what we eat.
- Consistent advice to follow includes:
- Eat a variety of foods.
- Increase fruits and vegetables.
- Drink lots of water.
- Slow down when you eat.
- Do your best to be mindful of when you start to feel full.
- Eat non-processed foods.

CHAPTER 27

DON'T FORGET
YOUR GOAL

———

Part of my mom's concern for me as a picky eater was my health. Her main goal was to have a happy, healthy child. That is where all of her concern really stemmed from. She worried whether or not I was healthy enough and getting all of my vitamins and minerals. She would take me to our pediatrician or doctor and they might recommend adding a few extra vitamins into my diet but otherwise, time after time they would say, "She is healthy. Don't worry about it. She will grow out of it."

I hardly ever missed a day of school from being sick and, in fact, for the majority of my school years had a perfect attendance record. I was athletic in high school as a varsity cheerleader as well as active in the marching band. I'm currently 5'2" and at a healthy weight for my build. If you look at me and my sisters together, you will see we are almost all the same height and weight. So my diet did not cause me to suffer from regular illnesses, stunted growth, or cause me to be significantly overweight or underweight or anything of the sort despite how many times I heard people tell me my diet was unhealthy and said how shocked they were I wasn't two hundred pounds on my carb and cheese "diet." I only say this to reassure parents of picky eaters. It is possible for your picky eater to be okay on a restricted diet. The goal is to have your picky eater be happy and reasonably healthy, not to have the perfect diet.

I know protein in particular was a concern for my mom because I wasn't eating any meat or eggs. I got most of my protein from nuts, milk, peanut butter and fruit.

During the summer of 2017 while I was staying at my parents' house after returning from Belgium, my dad came home and said, "Guess what? The National Health Organization just created a new supplement to distribute to refugees to ensure they are getting enough protein. Guess what the main ingredient is?"

I looked at him and asked what? He exclaimed, "It's peanut butter! The National Health Organization is putting the refugees on the "Jessie diet" to improve their health!"

For years and years I would have plain Cheerios for breakfast with milk, a PB&J for lunch with a fruit or snack and a grilled cheese or cheese quesadilla for dinner.

So let's think about this for a minute. How much protein do we really need on a daily basis? Did I really need to eat meat as often as everyone thought I should? Nope, I didn't. Was my diet really as "unhealthy" as everyone thought it was? Nope, it wasn't.

Was it the best it could be? No, certainly not. But it wasn't "bad" either, and in some cases was even better than some of my peers.

This was very interesting for me to discover. It is even more interesting trying to figure out what I WANT to eat now that I actually have a choice for WHAT to eat. I've researched the various ways we can get protein into our diet and how much we really "need."

Proteins are the main building blocks of your body. They are used to make muscles, tendons, organs and skin, as well as enzymes, hormones, neurotransmitters and various tiny molecules that serve many important functions. Proteins are made out of smaller molecules called amino acids, which are linked together like beads on a string. These linked amino acids form long protein chains, which are then folded into complex shapes. Some of these amino acids can be produced by your body while you must get others through your diet. The latter are called essential amino acids. Without protein, life as you know it would not be possible.

So yes we DO need protein in our diets, but how much and where we get it from can vary.

The DRI (Dietary Reference Intake) recommends 0.8 grams of protein per kilogram of body weight, or 0.36 grams per pound.[39]

This amounts to only about 10 percent of your daily calories or approximately:

- 56 grams per day for the average sedentary man.
- 46 grams per day for the average sedentary woman.

According to the latest data from the National Health and Nutrition Examination Survey, American women already eat about sixty-eight grams a day.

---

39 Gunnars, K. (2018). *Protein Intake – How Much Protein Should You Eat Per Day?*. [online] Healthline. Available at: https://www.health-line.com/nutrition/how-much-protein-per-day [Accessed 12 Jan. 2019].

"There's no reason to go out of your way to get protein," says Dariush Mozaffarian, MD, dean of the Tufts Friedman School of Nutrition Science & Policy. "Just eat a variety of fish, nuts, beans, seeds, and dairy, including yogurt." However, increasing your protein may make sense if you're very active or you're trying to lose weight.

You can get your protein from meat and eggs and you can also get your protein from fruits and vegetables or even from milk or peanut butter or nuts. We don't really need to have meat or fish with every single meal to have enough protein in our diet.

Here are ten high protein vegetables you could add into your diet:

- Peas
- Spinach
- Kale
- Broccoli
- Sprouts
- Mushrooms
- Artichokes
- Asparagus
- Corn

Here are ten high protein fruits you could add into your diet:

- Guavas
- Avocados
- Apricots
- Kiwi
- Blackberries
- Oranges
- Bananas
- Cantaloupe
- Raspberries
- Peaches

Here are ten high protein nuts you could add into your diet:

- Peanuts
- Almonds
- Pistachios
- Cashews
- Walnuts
- Hazelnuts
- Pine nuts
- Pecans
- Macadamia nuts
- Dried coconut

I found it fascinating to discover that Felix noticed similar circumstances to mine with regards to his clients' health. He said, "When I inquire about the child's health, it is not uncommon to hear 'He/she can get a bit tired on occasion, but otherwise fine. Even their doctor says their health is fine.' Now when I was brought up, I believed this idea that if we don't have a certain ratio of food, we will not function and could not survive. This is another myth. Regular feedback from my clients tells me otherwise, and not just with young kids, but often with adults well into their late twenties.

"If these people are not eating vegetables or fruit, or meat or fish, how can they even survive? Where are they getting their protein, carbs and fat from?

"The answer is that ALL food ultimately comes from plants. In every plant cell there will be: carbohydrates, protein, and fats. That's how herbivores also grow 'meat.' Through a concentration of all the basic ingredients already present in all plant cells. Sure, we are designed to be more omnivorous than such animals, but it has proven to be possible to survive, and even be in good-enough health, on a very, very limited diet.

"I have quite a few video testimonials of clients who are physically imposing—tall, athletic, and sporty looking only to be told that they have lived off one to three food items. As one mother told me, "My son is an eleven-year-old (strapping) boy who had SED from birth. He has only ever eaten: dry cereal, sometimes milk (separately); crisps, coco pops, popcorn, yogurt and biscuits." This is an extremely 'unhealthy' diet since birth and yet she goes on to add, 'He is of normal height and weight and his health is fine. In fact, he rarely gets colds or coughs.' Theories do not always match up to real life."

So don't worry too much about your picky eater's health unless there are clear physical signs and symptoms you and your doctor have noticed that are pointing you in that direction. People can survive and thrive off of less than what we have been led to believe. As long as your picky eater is happy, energetic and enjoying life, they are doing just fine.

Picky Points:

- Do not lose sight of your end goal—a healthy and happy child, not one with the perfect diet.
- Don't worry, it is possible for your picky eater to be okay on a restricted diet.
- You can find protein in in a variety of different foods.
- You don't need to eat meat as often as you'd think.

MASHED POTATOES

——

We've made it to mashed potatoes. We are now going to cook our potato in yet another different way by boiling it. With mashed potatoes we have now completely changed textures to a very soft, fluffy creamy texture. We still have the same potato taste that we have gotten used to but there is no crunch left at all. Mashed potatoes can be sticky, smooth, soft, creamy, or fluffy depending on how they are made. You are also eating them differently, mashed potatoes stick in your mouth and on your tounge which is quite different than a crispy crunchy french fry that you are munching on with your teeth.

INGREDIENTS

- 2 pounds Russet Potatoes
- 2 tablespoons Butter
- 1 cup Milk
- Salt
- Pepper

INSTRUCTIONS

1. Bring a pot of salted water to a boil.
2. Peel your potatoes and quarter them.
3. Add potatoes and cook until tender but still firm for about 15 minutes.
4. Drain the water from your pot.
5. In a small saucepan heat butter and milk over low heat until butter is melted.
6. Using a potato masher or electric beater, slowly blend milk mixture into potatoes until smooth and creamy
7. Season with salt and pepper to taste.

PART 7

AWARENESS AND CHANGE

In this section we take a look at what it really means to change. A lot of extremely picky eaters want to change their diet but feel as though it is impossible. I wanted more than anything to change, but I felt like I couldn't and had no idea where to start. For picky eaters there is the phobia of food that needs to be addressed, but to ensure you create lasting change, you have to do more than just remove the fear around food. You have to find your reason to change, create new behaviors with food, and build new eating habits. It has been really interesting looking back on how I was able to not only change my picky eating but also build a whole new diet.

And guess what? The strategies discussed in this section can be applied to anyone in any aspect of his or her life, not just for extremely picky eaters.

CHAPTER 28

WRITE IT DOWN

———

Once I had my breakthrough with Felix and was trying all these new foods, my sisters got me a health tracking journal and a goal tracking journal.

The small health tracking journal had "eat... drink... move... sleep" on the front and helped me record my daily health practices, hours slept, exercise, what I ate and drank that day, and ways to destress so I could stay on top of my goals, build better habits and feel my very best.

It's a very simple straightforward journal with a few lines for weekly goals and some space to track your meals, snacks, water, exercise, sleep and stress relief for each day. That's it.

The goal tracking journal was a BestSelf Co journal, which helps keep you focused and on track for achieving your goals. It's a very well-organized journal, which helps you clearly identify what you want to focus on each day and brings some awareness to your morning and evening routine. In the Best-Self Co journal, you outline your goals, daily schedule, targets for the day, lessons learned, wins and what you are grateful for. It helped me stay focused on my goals to try new foods.

These were both great tools as I worked toward my goal to expand my diet. There are also lots of different phone apps available now that make it quick and easy to track your food, drinks, exercise and sleep!

In the health tracking journal, there were lines to fill out what you ate for each meal and a section to outline your goals for the week. It wasn't too hard to start with tracking what I ate for breakfast, lunch and dinner. Just one quick line to fill in. In the goal section I would identify two or three new foods I wanted to try for the week. That took some planning and I had to make sure to buy the new food ahead of time and figure out how to eat or cook it. At the end of each week there was a space with three questions.

- "Challenges?"
- "Achievements?"
- "How am I feeling physically and mentally?"

The result of these questions really surprised me!

The challenges section was very helpful because at least if you didn't achieve what you planned you could identify why. Once you know what your challenges are, you can create a better plan and overcome them next time. This way you can see what your own personal stumbling blocks are. Then next week you just set your goals and try again!

It was always great filling out the achievements section when I tried something new for the week or had the opportunity to try something completely unexpected at a lunch or dinner with friends! It provides a moment of reflection to take a look at what you are doing right and I always felt a deep sense of pride with each new food I was able to try!

The most interesting was figuring out how I felt physically and mentally for that week. I would take a moment to actually check in with myself and ask this question. I started to notice differences in how I felt and would look back over what I had been eating and drinking that week. What was important with this was discovering for myself what was going on with my body depending on what I ate and drank.

For ten days I tried fruit smoothies in the morning. I was shocked at how much more energy I had, how much lighter I felt, how my skin looked better AND how hungry I was by 10:30 a.m. I also realized I didn't really want the same smoothie every day. So certain aspects of my morning smoothie I liked and some I didn't. I liked having more energy and was glad to be getting good nutrients from the fruit, but I didn't like that I was still hungry in the morning after just a few hours with a smoothie for breakfast. But now I had the information to figure out what to do next. I added other filling ingredients to my smoothies or would add a little something extra to my breakfast on the side. I would continue to have them but not every single morning and would alternate with a few other breakfast options. You are essentially tracking your own personal experiments with food.

I started paying attention to how I felt at the end of each day or after each meal. I'd just take a moment to ask myself how I felt after each breakfast, lunch, or dinner. I would notice some meals made me super drowsy afterward or uncomfortably full. Others, I'd feel okay. Some I'd feel great and full of energy. I started to notice changes when I would try a new food. All meat was new to me because none of it fell under one of my comfort foods as a picky eater.

Bacon was the first meat I tried because I noticed that bacon was a comfort food for a lot of other extremely picky eaters since it is so salty and crunchy. The first week I tried bacon I noticed that by the end of the week I was starting to break out. That wasn't normal for me and so I was pretty surprised.

More new information. Would my body just get used to it or would I be more likely to break out when I ate bacon in the future? I didn't know. Even if I did continue to break out at least I would be aware of what was going on. I would know if I had a slice of bacon every once in a while, I probably wouldn't break out but if I had it every day for a week or more I probably would. It's just good to know and it's completely different for every single person.

One thing I hear a lot is, "I don't have the time to keep a journal." It is true that it does take time, but how much is completely up to you. It doesn't actually have to take that much time. You don't have to spend an hour in the morning journaling. It took me about five minutes to decide what my food goals would be at the beginning of each week. Then a minute or two to write what I ate each day and then another eight minutes or so to write down my challenges, achievements, and how I felt at the end of each week. I bet if you want to, you could start by finding two minutes during the day to write down what you ate that day.

Robin Mizaur, who we hear more from in the last chapter of this section, also encourages journaling. She said, "I think it's really interesting when I ask people to write down everything they eat for three days and show them what they wrote at the end of the three days. It helps put things in perspective and brings some awareness."

Robin had a client named Deborah who told her, "I love sweets. I could eat cake and cookies all day long." Robin suggested to her, "Okay, let's break this down daily. Do you eat your sweets in the morning or in the afternoon? Do you honestly have something sweet like that every single day?" She said, "Let's pick one day a week where you don't eat anything sweet." So they did and started with no sweets on Mondays.

Robin mentioned to me, "It has to be just one small thing to start." After just 2 weeks Deborah was up to 2 full days of no sweets and said to her, "You know, I feel better on those days."

Robin excitedly told me, "I was so happy to hear Deborah tell me, 'I didn't realize the sweets were affecting me this way.' So I said, 'Well, would you like to feel better on any other days besides those two days?' and then we started taking the sweets out of other days during the week as well."

She said, "Just getting people to realize that they have control over what they eat and that they can heal themselves is a wonderful thing."

The National Heart, Lung and Blood Institute at the National Institutes of Health funded Kaiser Permanente's Center for Health Research to conduct one of the largest and longest weight-loss maintenance trials.

The study involved more than 1,600 people, which was published in the *American Journal of Preventive Medicine,* found that those who kept daily food journals consumed fewer calories, resulting in twice as much weight loss over six months as those who did not keep journals. The study indicated that about 70 percent of participants lost enough weight to lower their health risks because they kept track of what they ate daily.[40]

Not only does journaling have great benefits when it comes to your health, diet and what you are eating, but there are so many additional benefits to journaling as well with just a few of them being:

- Stress reduction
- Emotional healing and intelligence
- Personal growth and development
- Better problem solving
- Getting to know yourself better
- Capturing your life story
- Achieving your goals
- Evoking awareness and mindfulness
- Enhanced intuition and creativity

---

40 Sass, C. (2014). *6 Fascinating Things a Food Journal Can Teach You About Your Eating Habits.* [online] Health. Available at: https://www.health.com/nutrition/6-fascinating-things-a-food-journal-can-teach-you-about-your-eating-habits [Accessed 12 Jan. 2019].

- Strengthened self-discipline
- Improved communication skills

According to the Health.com article "6 Fascinating Things a Food Journal Can Teach You about Your Eating Habits," by Cynthia Saas, MPH, RD you can discover:

- Why you eat when you aren't hungry?
- How your dining companions affect your habits?
- How much you're really eating?
- How fast you chow down?
- How you feel after eating certain foods?
- Do your perceptions match reality?

There are numerous articles out there with the benefits of journaling. It can make a huge difference not only in your health and eating habits but in any aspect of your life as you implement change.

Picky Points:

- Keep a health tracking journal. Write down your goals and what you are eating.
- Keep track of how you feel after each week, each day or each meal.
- Keep it simple. You don't have to spend an hour a day on it. Just jot down a few quick notes.

- Ask yourself questions before, during and after you eat to broaden your awareness. Has your energy increased or decreased? Did you experience any side effects?

CHAPTER 29

START WITH ONE SMALL STEP!

———

"One small change in your diet and one small change in your fitness regimen. That's all it takes." ~Travis Johnson

Travis Johnson is an experienced Investor, Chief Executive Officer, Mentor and founder of foodjunky.com (now part of delivery.com), an online food ordering and delivery business.

"I was the guy who came from the Midwest, ate meat three times a day and enjoyed it," said Travis. When he left to go to college at the University of Colorado Boulder, things started to change. When he got to college he discovered that his roommate was vegan. His first instinct was to make jokes about his roommate's diet because it was different. However, he didn't expect to find out that it was in fact his own eating habits that were different from those around him.

As a young adult his diet basically consisted of typical American, Italian and Chinese dishes with mostly meat and fried items. He would eat a lot of Kit Kats and other chocolate bars but usually didn't have too many other desserts. He always considered himself someone who would eat anything even though there were several things he stayed away from such as beets, yogurt, cheesecake, jelly filled anything (besides PB&J), nuts, custards and any other nonstandard dessert.

His new roommate and the health conscious culture in Boulder helped to create a new awareness for Travis around his diet, health and food. As he said, "What I was doing was the odd thing and so I slowly changed." He always knew there were vegan and vegetarian options available he just was never interested in them. However, he was suddenly immersed in a very health-conscious city with a health-conscious roommate. So he changed.

Now Travis usually only eats meat three times a week instead of three times a day, is very athletic and is a nationally ranked Triathlete competing in Ironman distance races. He signed up for his first 5K back in 2003. However, he hurt his ankle so he never ran the race. It wasn't for a couple of years that he learned he was running incorrectly (heal striking instead of toe striking) and decided to try again.

He did his first sprint triathlon in 2005. This time he ran the race and finished. Ever since then it's always been about pushing to find his limits. To sprint, swim, and bike in a triathlon. It is important to pay attention to your diet and your body, and he started paying even closer attention to what he was eating. He has been tracking and logging his food for years now and is aware on any given day if he is over or under his desired caloric intake so he can perform at his best.

He emphasized to me how fitness is an integral part of diet, even if it is just your daily step goal.

He said, "Those steps are also part of my diet. People change slowly. It's hard and it takes time to start eating healthy. But once you are eating healthy, it is also hard to go back and eat unhealthy!"

As human beings we tend to delay action to the point of reward, which is the basis for procrastination. We don't take action until there is a clear reward and reason for doing so. Delayed gratification, where you resist a smaller more immediate reward for a larger or more enduring reward later, is a hard concept for a lot of people. Especially in our current fast paced culture where everyone is looking for immediate gratification. With our diet and health, it is very hard to delay the action to the point of reward because it is such a long time before you get to see the reward and experience the benefits from it.

It's the idea of foregoing that second serving at dinner or passing up on the extra chips or candy today so that four weeks from now you are able to meet your weight loss goal. Especially with food, it is so much more rewarding to your taste buds to dive into the chips bag right now. We all know that by doing so we will lose out on our long-term health goals, but sometimes we do it anyway because we don't see the effect of that decision until much later. Then "all of a sudden" we are overweight, are exhausted all the time, are addicted to unhealthy food, are depressed, or god forbid, wake up in the hospital with heart disease, diabetes, cancer or other serious health complications.

You don't see the immediate results with food and exercise like you do in other areas of your life, but there will be results from your decisions and actions today.

The good news is we can change our behaviors and as Travis puts it, "We are all animals. We are all trainable."

He has explored how we can rethink our associations with food and exercise to help us succeed with changing our food habits. He says to flip how we think about our relationship between food and exercise and shift the reward.

He suggests, "Instead of thinking, 'I shouldn't have eaten that brownie and now I should go work out to make up for it,' try thinking, 'I'm going to go work out today and then consciously say, I'll treat myself to a brownie afterward.'

"So you can have the exact same one mile and one brownie, but you will feel completely different about them both by flipping your association between them. The funny thing is after working out you feel so good that it becomes a rare occurrence for you to actually reach for that brownie or unhealthy treat afterward. It is just psychology."

He says, "You need to start listening to your body, stop over-eating and start figuring out where your equilibrium is."

I asked him how someone should start changing their food habits and he replied, "The best way to do that is slowly and cut one thing at a time. First step, I suggest you cut the calories out of the liquids." So that means no soft drinks.

His question to us is, "Can you do that one thing consciously and consistently? Once you do, it will gradually become a subconscious ingrained habit and then you can begin changing another new behavior consciously."

It has commonly been said that it takes twenty-one days to form a habit, but I've found that is not necessarily true. You can both form a habit a lot quicker than twenty-one days or a lot slower than twenty-one days. It completely depends on the consistency and frequency in which you are implementing the new habit.

As Maria Brilaki says, "Here's the loophole I see right away: What is meant by a habit? What type of behavior are you trying to make a habit? Because surely going from seven to eight glasses of water a day is going to be different than going from three to eight. And both of those will feel different when switching from waking up at 9 a.m. to waking up at 8 a.m. And again all of those will be different from trying to replace your cookie comfort-eating habit with carrots."[41]

Maria is the founder of Fitness Reloaded, where she helps over 100,000 monthly readers make better, healthier choices. She's a Stanford Engineering grad and the best-selling author of *Surprisingly…Unstuck: The Power of Small Healthy Habits in a World Addicted to Instant Results.*

41 Brilaki, M. (2017). *How Many Days Does It Take To Form A Habit? 'Not 21,' Science Says..* [online] Fitness Reloaded. Available at: https://fitnessreloaded.com/how-many-days-to-form-a-habit/ [Accessed 12 Jan. 2019].

In her article she says, "Not all habits are created equal and the time it takes for a behavior to become a habit will depend on a multitude of different factors, including:

- complexity of the new activity
- how it fits in your routine
- how often you practice it
- individual differences

Just think about this for a second; which of the two would you find easier to start doing:

1. Drinking a glass of water with breakfast in the morning or
2. Going for an hour-long run moments after you roll out of bed?"

Yeah, that's what I thought—the water. So the complexity of the behavior matters."

It's not just me saying this either; there is science to support it too.

- In 2006, Verplanken gave students one of two writing tasks. The first group simply had to underline 'She/she' every time they came across it in a piece of text. The other group had the more complex task to underline all words referencing a moveable object or mammal. What they found was that the simple task became more autonomous by the end of the study, indicating that they're quicker/easier to become habitual.

- A little more recently, Lally et al., recruited students to choose a health-related behavior they wanted to develop into a habit. The students chose behaviors like doing fifty sit-ups with their morning coffee, eating a piece of fruit with lunch, and drinking a glass of water with their lunch. What they found was that developing an exercise habit took one and a half times longer than an eating or drinking habit, which they suggested was because the eating/drinking behaviors were much simpler than the exercise ones.

"The more frequently and consistently you do something, the sooner it will become autonomous. For example, you can't expect to pick up a habit like going to the gym if you're only doing it once every month. The same goes for any other behaviors; the more frequently you do them, the quicker they're likely to become a habit."

Just starting to be mindful of what you are eating and drinking can change everything. It doesn't have to be overwhelming and it doesn't have to take a lot of time. There are a few very simple things you can start to do today to be more aware. One small change is all it takes.

Picky Points:

- Become mindful and conscious of your food choices and make them habitual.
- Not all habits are created equal, a less complex habit can be formed quicker than you'd think.
- Make one small change today.
- Drink an extra glass of water with your meal.
- Add in one fruit with lunch.
- Take a look at the food labels of what you eat today.
- Write down what you eat today.

CHAPTER 30

ONE CHANGE CAN LEAD TO MANY!

———

"I cut one thing out and it totally changed my world. In my experience true health comes at the intersection of self-discovery and intentional living." ~Elizabeth Moore

Elizabeth Moore is the cofounder of TRILUNA Wellness + Events, a company that specialized in practical, everyday health that operates out of Nashville, Tennessee. After battling an eating disorder and suffering from food allergies with headaches, anxiety and severe intestinal issues and trying lots of different yo-yo diets, including Weight Watchers, Elizabeth was at her wits' end. She was miserable and had a lot of anxiety and frustration with food and her diet because of her digestive issues.

One of her friends suggested she cut out gluten in the fall of 2010 and by Thanksgiving she was completely gluten free. It was difficult to navigate and she realized that a lot more food than she originally thought had gluten in it.

She said, "Giving up gluten was incredibly difficult, but I felt so dramatically better at the time that going back wasn't an option for me. I started by taking out the big stuff: beer, bread, crackers. All the really obvious stuff. Over the course of the first few months I kept telling myself I was making it up, but then I would eat something with gluten and I would get really sick. It wasn't easy.

"Gluten free pizza just wasn't the same and we didn't have access to all the gluten free options like we do now, so for the most part I just gave it all up. Pastries, pizza, pasta. It just wasn't worth it to me at the time. I found it easier to do once I made the connection to how it was making me feel. I recognized that this was, for me, a time of healing. It was a time to get to know my body, to listen to it, and to really figure out what I needed. I tried to respect that without getting too obsessed with what was going into my body. Because of my history with eating disorders, I could get really dogmatic and strict about my diet really fast. It wasn't healthy at first, but once I started to listen more to my body rather than obsessing over it, my strict diet leveled out."

In just a few months after cutting out gluten Elizabeth had lost twenty pounds. Not only that but what it really did was create an awareness of what she was putting into her body. It was her very first intentional step toward changing her health and it meant she had to start reading labels and change her food habits.

She became very curious about processed foods, foraged and local foods, vitamins, meditation, and the science behind some of the fad diets. The more she researched the more she knew she was heading in the right direction toward something that was truly going to change her life.

In 2014 she studied with the Institute of Integrative Nutrition and became certified as a health coach. In 2015 she knew this was the path for her. She quit her job in marketing to help her friends, Jess Rice and Susannah Herring, open up a raw/vegan restaurant in Nashville, Tennessee, called AVO where she was able to hone her chef skills. In October of that same year she won Amy Rachelle's PURERAW scholarship to a detox and raw foods chef training program in Bali, Indonesia, where they juice fasted and learned more about the inner workings of the body and how our bodies are affected by the world around us.

Then in 2017 she completed a two-hundred-hour Kali Yuga Yoga training and started TRILUNA with her business partner, Ashley Brooke James, to promote healthy living and coach other women who've experienced the same frustrations and anxiety with food, fitness, and their bodies.

Elizabeth says, "Our relationship with food as a nation is problematic at best. I'm a fan of going back to basics. The more disconnected you are from your food, the more it's just stuff that's going into your mouth instead of nourishment. Our food is so tied to our belief systems and who we are. It's never just the food."

Going gluten free was kind of like the gateway drug to Elizabeth's food journey, completely drawing her into the food world. This one small step helped her move out of her current eating habits and into a whole new healthier lifestyle.

She told me, "The change is always a slow burn. There's no such thing as 'getting there,' you just get better at listening intuitively to your body and figuring out what makes you feel good physically and emotionally."

As Elizabeth put it, "We are creatures of habit. Becoming aware of our habits is 90 percent of the battle."

In 2017, Elizabeth had a really exciting trip for Rome, Italy, planned! At that point after being gluten free for seven years, she had started experimenting with gluten again, introducing it slowly. She started with sourdough from a recommended local bakery and then started to make her own sourdough bread. Then she started slowly introducing other things that she knew had small amounts of gluten, such as sauces and dips, soy sauce for example. She used digestive enzymes and introduced things slowly and then waited and listened to her body.

There are a lot of common foods containing gluten in Italy such as pastas, noodles, breads, pastries, crackers, baked goods, cereal, granola, pancakes, waffles, crepes, biscuits, croutons, flour tortillas, flour sauces and gravies. By the time she went to Rome she was ready to try it all. So many delicious temptations around every corner. Although she'd been slowly reintroducing for a while, it was nothing like the scale of Rome. She hadn't eaten pasta or bread that wasn't sourdough but knew she was ready to try.

She said, "The first day I arrived in Rome I had risotto, which is rice, so it is naturally gluten free and I had decided that I was going to try and find gluten free options as much as possible while I was in Italy. But nope. One morning I saw this beautiful flakey little croissant and at that exact moment smelled the coffee as I walked in and just knew that was what I wanted and was ready to try it. So I did. I had a salad for lunch that day so it wouldn't interfere with my experiment but by dinner that night I still felt fine. Usually the results were immediate—like, oh no, I got into some gluten and I'd know right away that my body didn't agree with it. For dinner that night I had pasta and I felt great. No digestive issues, no heartburn, nothing. Just blissfully happy and full."

She had dreaded how her body was going to react but shockingly enough she actually felt okay afterward! She was thrilled! She could have coffee with croissants again after seven years of no gluten! She dug in a little more to figure out what was going on. Surely these croissants have gluten and her body should have reacted to them. So why wasn't it?

She researched and learned a lot about the science of baking bread and her understanding of it is that most bread in America is so over processed that our body has access to the gluten easier and so it creates greater side effects. It takes Elizabeth three days to make her homemade sourdough bread, so it's a process but it's fun and worth it. She loves it and her body does too! The key for Elizabeth is that when she experiments with something new, she records what happens and listens to her own body.

According to Grainstorm a lot has changed with our wheat in the last few generations. They say, "Grain has been at the heart of humankind's diet for thousands of years. It is, in fact, the foundation of civilization: it cultivates easily, stores for years in kernel form, releasing its nutritional bounty when the seed is ground and prepared into fresh breads or porridges. This is how grains have been consumed over the millennia: stored in whole kernel form and milled fresh, full of life and nutrients. For ten thousand years, we cultivated wheat, stored it, milled it and consumed it. The system worked, and it nourished civilization.[42]

"And yet it's very clear to us: modern wheat is making people sick. More and more people are going gluten-free to fix long-standing digestion issues and they feel better. Yet, it is also very clear that there is more to this than gluten. For instance, we get many people telling us how they can't eat gluten so they eat spelt or Kamut. Yet both these ancient grains have gluten.

"So what's changed? In fact, almost everything. The way we grow it, the way we process it and the way we eat. The very wheat itself. Since industrialization, everything has changed, and it has happened in two distinct 'technology revolutions.' The first was in milling, the second in cultivation and farming. Both have had a profound effect, yet most people have no idea.

---

42 GRAINSTORM. (2019). *What's wrong with modern wheat.* [online] Available at: https://grainstorm.com/pages/modern-wheat [Accessed 12 Jan. 2019].

"There is an increasingly understood distinction between gluten intolerance and modern wheat sensitivity, yet as more and more people go gluten-free, many are unaware of the difference. We have waves of people (with varying degrees of wheat sensitivity) going gluten-free to be healthier. And the food industry is responding. A dizzying selection of gluten-free products has popped up, seemingly overnight, to cater to this new 'healthy' lifestyle choice.

"For the vast majority of gluten-free eaters that do not have celiac disease, we propose a return to honest to goodness old fashioned flour: organic heritage wheats, freshly stone ground. You need to look for stone-ground "whole meal" flour, where the entire wheat kernel is ground and the germ is crushed into the flour."

Michael Pollan says in his food documentary, *Cooked*, "I would bet that if you took a dozen people who claimed gluten intolerance and you gave them Richard's bread, they'd be fine." The bread he is referring to is a sourdough made the old fashioned way, with hours of fermentation and naturally occurring yeast found in the air by a baker named Richard Bourdon in rural Massachusetts. Bourdon and Pollan go on to explain the importance of proper fermentation of grains to aid in digestion.

Pollan says, "A long fermentation process allows bacteria to fully break down the carbohydrates and gluten in bread, making it easier to digest and releasing the nutrients within it, allowing our bodies to more easily absorb them. Pollan hypothesizes that speeding up the bread-making process for mass consumption has so radically altered what we know as bread in the last century that it's no longer as easily digested."

In 2011, a small study conducted in Italy tried giving volunteers with celiac disease a small amount of specially prepared sourdough bread. The subjects in the study seemed to react well to the sourdough, which had been fermented until the gluten within it was degraded. The study concluded that the bread was not toxic to the celiac disease subjects.[43]

Elizabeth says, "I am now almost completely back on the gluten bandwagon. I make my own sourdough bread at home and eat a lot of it. I bake a lot. Biscuits, pizza crust, hand pies, cakes, cookies. I've thrown myself into learning how to bake with real flour now that I am no longer afraid of it. It's

43 Greco, L., Gobbetti, M., Auricchio, R., Di Mase, R., Landolfo, F., Paparo, F., Di Cagno, R., De Angelis, M., Rizzello, C., Cassone, A., Terrone, G., Timpone, L., D'Aniello, M., Maglio, M., Troncone, R. and Auricchio, S. (2011). Safety for Patients With Celiac Disease of Baked Goods Made of Wheat Flour Hydrolyzed During Food Processing. *Clinical Gastroenterology and Hepatology*, 9(1), pp.24-29.

been such a pleasure getting to bake again; I love it so much. I even teach a cooking/baking class with real flour—sweet and savory hand pies. I'm even taking a croissant making class so I can give the gift of those flakey little perfections to my friends and loved ones."

Elizabeth reminded me that, "Every single body is different and every single body needs a different set of foods and habits to make them healthy and whole."

Although going gluten-free was the start of Elizabeth's journey, it is certainly not the end. Gluten is possible again for Elizabeth and she has learned so much about her health and nutrition along the way. Eliminating the gluten from Elizabeth's diet opened her eyes and broadened her awareness. Seeing and understanding how the food she was eating was affecting her body and her life made her curious to find out more. It is not always easy but it is possible and you just need to make one small change to start. That one change can lead to many and before you know you will have created massive change in your life.

When I asked Elizabeth what her advice would be to anyone trying to change their relationship with food she said, "Eat close to the earth, seasonally, do your best, don't eat with guilt, enjoy your food, and eat with friends."

Picky Points:

- One small change to your diet can lead to massive change in your life.
- Becoming aware of your habits is 90 percent of the battle.
- If you have a modern wheat sensitivity consider looking into old-fashioned stone ground flour.
- Listen to your body and figure out what makes you feel good physically and emptionally.

CHAPTER 31

CHANGE YOURSELF FIRST

"The changes we make with our diet are probably the single most important thing we can do to determine our destiny." ~Dr. Michelle McMacken, MD, Assistant Professor of Medicine, NYU School of Medicine.

We have the power to really impact each other's relationship with food. It can be hard to change our food habits but with the support of one another it can become much easier.

Robin Mizaur is a former United States Marine Corps Soldier, a certified Personal Trainer, Nutritional Consultant and a Holistic Life Coach specializing in Wellness. Robin is one of the founders of HappyNash.com, a community dedicated to teach and deliver a daily dose of healthy lifestyle habits.

Robin was previously living and working in Chicago where she managed wellness clinics and worked with cancer patients. While she was there they opened several multi-million-dollar wellness centers. She's worked with thousands of people on nutrition and holistic healing through their facilities.

As Robin Mizaur says, "People want to have what you have and can sense it. They want more energy. They don't want to be tired when they wake up, and they want to sleep better."

Robin has been juicing for thirty years. When she started juicing thirty years ago, her family thought she was weird but now they are coming around after years and years of watching her juice. Robin has found it can sometimes actually be harder to help the intimate people in your life than to help people you've just met. She said she is the kind of person who implements change quickly. But not everyone is like that. She said, "If I know something is really good, I'm going to jump in with both feet."

One weekend, Robin and her husband had visitors from Chicago stay with them. She said, "I don't change my eating habits when we have visitors stay with us. I just do what makes me feel good. So I juiced and prepared everything as I normally would for our meals. When our guests saw how much energy I had and that what we were eating tasted good, they wanted to try it too. I actually wound up coaching them."

She remembers when she first starting changing her family's diet. Her kids were ten and twelve and she was told her son had ADHD and that he needed medication. She immediately started researching and changing what they were eating.

She said, "When you are dealing with young children, you have to realize it isn't an easy change but it will influence them for the better if they see their parents with more energy and feeling better. I remember they were addicted to pop and I created a challenge for our family for fourteen days to not drink any more pop. My kids became more invested in the challenge then we were. One of the kids called me one day to tell me that Dad had a pop when he wasn't supposed to. It was interesting to see the dynamic change. The kids were policing us instead of us trying to change them. We all stopped drinking diet pop after that."

I asked Robin what advice she would give when someone asks her what they could do right now to start changing?

She said, "Start reading labels and try to eventually move toward eating things that don't have a label. If you stop drinking diet soda and drink more water, you're winning.

Robin said, "I think it's exciting when people realize they can start in the next fifteen minutes. I think just explaining to people how important it is to hydrate your body with good water is a great place to start. It's one of the first things I talk with people about. How it detoxes your cells and how you can start drinking more water immediately.

"You don't have to wait until next week at the grocery store. You can do something now. Another one you can start right away is reading the labels on your food. For just one thing that you eat today, turn it over and read the label. It is quick, easy and you can do it right now. Those two things can be pivotal points in someone's life to help someone get excited and start changing immediately."

Robin says, "We are big on the education part and huge advocates of getting the right knowledge and skills to the community before they become clients at our cancer centers. You need to get to the younger generation and it can be hard because people want that instant gratification. Especially with food. It's important to make it simple with something they can do and start immediately. Have them ask themselves, 'What can I do today to make myself feel better and have more energy?'"

Another thing Robin encourages is intermittent fasting. She says fasting doesn't have to be as difficult as you might think. You could just go from 6 p.m. until 10 a.m. and that's a sixteen-hour fast. You'll see immediate results.

By the way, did you know that night fasting is the origination for where the word breakfast came from. You would wake up in the morning and break your night fast with your first meal or breakfast! That's an example of a lifestyle change with quick results that can be followed up with factual research and information now to get someone interested and ready to change.

My mom said, "I've been trying to be more conscious lately because of you girls. You got me into the smoothie kick and I'm drinking more coconut water because of your sister. Plus I hear the doctors telling my mom to have less salt in her diet to help with her heart. So I've also started to cut back on the salt in my diet and look more carefully at what I eat."

I would make a smoothie almost every morning for breakfast and would ask Mom if she would like a little and when she said, "Sure!" I'd give her a little glass with some of my smoothie in it. Now I've moved to Nashville but the smoothie habit has stuck and my mom will still make a fresh smoothie every few days. She's a great example of implementing change for those she loves one step at a time.

My mom has always loved food! Food is an integral part of her life and ever since she was a little girl she would wake up and ask Grandma, "What are we having for dinner?" If the answer was something she liked, she would skip out the door with a smile and she would look forward to it all throughout the school day. Especially if it was her absolute favorite home-cooked meal of Grandma's Sunday sauce with homemade meatballs or a nice turkey dinner! She was always so excited to come home for dinner and smell the food cooking.

It would go the other way too sometimes and she would be terribly disappointed if she found out they were going to be having macaroni and peas for dinner, which she never really liked.

Over the course of many years my mom has taught herself how to cook. When she started learning how to cook on her own, she was curious about how to cook the Sunday sauce herself because she loved Grandma's Sunday sauce so much as a child. She now makes an incredible Sunday sauce with meatballs and sausage and a lasagna that is an all-day cooking affair and is amazing!

She says, "I learned how to do it by trial and error. In the beginning, when I first married Dad, the sauce was thin and not very flavorful. So I kept calling up Grandma and asking things like, "What spices do you put in? How much water is needed? How long do you cook it?" Then I would experiment with what she told me, and then taste it, and repeat over and over again. Eventually it morphed into what I remembered eating as a child and now I'm really happy with it!" The Sunday sauce and lasagna with ricotta and meatballs and sausage is one of our favorite family recipes and is our Christmas dinner tradition!

We are inspired to learn how to cook the things we want to eat. This is true, time and time again. Those childhood recipes that we grow up loving are a great place to start. That's why it can be so powerful to let your child pick something at the market they want to try or a recipe they want to cook. If it's something they want to eat and choose themselves, they will be so much more invested in learning how to prepare and cook it.

As my mom says, "You are what you eat. Home cooking gives you a choice and the control for what ingredients you put in your food. When you cook at home, you know what you are eating. My motto is 'Do everything in moderation.' I live by that."

I want my family and friends to be healthy. I want them to live long and happy lives just as I am sure this is what my family and friends want for me. It is important to note though that no matter how many times my mom and dad would ask me to try something new as I was growing up I couldn't. It wasn't because I didn't love them. It wasn't because I didn't want to. I just wasn't able to change at that point. I didn't know I had a phobia of food. I didn't understand why. All I knew was that I just couldn't.

Even when someone isn't a picky eater with a phobia of food, no matter how many times you suggest someone change and try a new healthy food or recipe, they won't unless they are ready and want to change. Unfortunately, logic does not really work here. You can repeatedly tell someone why something is good or bad for him or her but until they decide to change it will fall on deaf ears. By the time most of us have graduated college, we have heard that fruits and vegetables are healthy—and chips and fast food are unhealthy. This is not new information. And yet, people still have trouble eating more vegetables and less chips. People have a general awareness of what they should or should not eat to stay healthy but that knowledge does not translate to their actions around food and diet unless they have a strong motivating factor to change and know how to successfully implement change.

There are four stages you go through when changing your health habits or behavior.[44] The four stages are:

1. Contemplation: "I'm thinking about it."
2. Preparation: "I've made up my mind to take action."
3. Action: "I have started to make changes."
4. Maintenance: "I have a new routine.""

The extremely picky eater in your life might be in the contemplation stage but not ready to take action yet. The absolute best that you can do in these situations is to focus on changing yourself and be a good example and inspiration for others. You can understand the different stages of change and determine which stage you are in. Learn your personal habit loops and how to modify them. It will be well worth the time you put in. Not only for the wonderful changes you will be making in your own life but for the numerous other people you will be able to help either directly or indirectly because of it. When someone you care about sees how much better you feel, how much happier you are, and how much energy you have they will want to have that too. They will be curious about what you are doing that is different from what they are doing.

---

44 Miller, C. (2017). *Changing Your Habits for Better Health | NIDDK.* [online] National Institute of Diabetes and Digestive and Kidney Diseases. Available at: https://www.niddk.nih.gov/health-information/diet-nutrition/changing-habits-better-health [Accessed 12 Jan. 2019].

As Chales Duhigg, the author of *The Power of Habit: Why We Do What We Do in Life and Business* said, "Change might not be fast and it isn't always easy. But with time and effort, almost any habit can be reshaped."

Picky Points:

- You cannot make your picky eater change. They have to want to change.
- Before you can help someone else, focus on changing yourself.
- There are 4 stages of change: contemplation, preparation, action and maintenance.
- Change yourself authentically and you can't help but influence those around you.

CHAPTER 32

FIND A REASON
TO CHANGE

———

"When people are faced with a life-changing illness, they usually fall into two different groups of people. One group of people want to do whatever it takes to heal their bodies, and another group of people don't want to change anything. If you continue to do what you have been doing, nothing will change." ~Robin Mizaur

Robin was a picky eater when she was younger. She only ate two or three things growing up and was eating the same things every day. Her parents would yell and scream at her to try something and "eat what she was given" but she said, "I could sit at that table all night without touching what they wanted me to eat." She was twelve or thirteen when she realized she didn't like the way she felt. She doesn't remember exactly when she had that conscious realization she just remembers not feeling good.

She said, "I didn't know what it was but I knew I needed to change something." After that when she would go grocery shopping with her mom or dad, she'd point to things at the store and say, "Can we try that?"

She was playing softball and wanted to be a better athlete. She knew what she was eating wasn't going to make her stronger. She is small at 4'10" and people often would tell her she couldn't do something and she always took that as a challenge and would think, "Oh yes I can."

There are a couple of distinct moments in her life when it became apparent to her just how important it was to have a well-rounded diet. One was when she joined the Marine Corps and said, "Being in the military really made me conscious of what I was eating because they feed you crap there." The other was when she became a parent and thought, "I have this little baby in me and I need to feed it well."

"Everyone has a passion, interest and love of something. As a child a lot of it usually stems from sports, schoolwork, or creativity. If you can find out what the love of your picky eater's life is right now, you can help influence them. And that can change daily with young kids, but try to find out what that is right now. Is it a sport? Do they want to be a better wrestler, dancer, or soccer player? Is it a hobby? Is it drawing or painting? Is it a person or a pet? You have to find something they relate to and then show them how nutritionally different foods could help to improve whatever their passion is."

"What are they focused on right now?" Robin worked with a young man named Adam and she said, "He wanted to have a starting position on the football team. We started with the fact that he was lifting weights to become stronger. Then we explored what else could make him stronger and talked about muscles and how they work and what nutrients your muscles need to become stronger. With Adam it was talking about what he thinks he would need to do to be to become better. It was a choice coming from him, his desire to want to change his eating habits and become better at what he's passionate about."

Robin says, "A lot of people don't know they have control over their health and their body. You're opening up a door for people. I think the journey to nutrition should be exciting for people. We have to encourage people with love and tear back those layers on why they think certain ways about food. When you change what you put in your body, it changes every relationship you have."

One of the things she explains to her clients is that what they put in their body helps determine their joy in life and their energy, and it can help them become a better spouse, mother, or father. The people who come to her to change are not just people who want to lose weight, they are also people who are lacking joy in their life or people who are lacking love for themselves.

When Robin has a new client, she has a pretty extensive questionnaire that she will ask her client to go through. Someone will come to her and say, "I want to lose fifteen pounds," and one of the questions she'll ask them is why? Why now?

She has found that most people change for a reason other than themselves. So what motivates someone to change?

Love. Love of someone or something is the biggest motivating force for change. Pain. When the pain of not changing becomes so intense, people will change.

Why is that? It's because change is about so much more than just logic. It is about psychology, your habits, your values, and your motivation.

For some, it may simply be a lack of knowledge for how to change or just a matter of breaking down their habit loops and putting a new behavior between their current cues and rewards. For others, their current situation may not be painful enough yet to make them feel like they really need to change.

Some may be struggling to change because they don't have a deeper motivation to change. They haven't dug deep enough to realize why they really want to change. What is their real reason to change? Is that reason strong enough to keep them motivated? What is something they really want? This has to do with their values and beliefs.

For example, take the question why do you want to lose weight?

It is one thing to say, "I want to lose weight because I don't feel good and I want to be healthier." It is an entirely different thing to say, "I want to lose weight because currently I'm on a high risk path for diabetes, stroke or heart disease and I want be around for a long time and grow old with my husband. To be there for him, to laugh and cry together as we watch our children grow up. I want to be alive and healthy when my children need my advice, see them get married, and support them as they have children of their own. I want to have the energy and ability to run around and play and laugh with them." The first reason is valid but the second is tapping into your feelings and love for your family.

Your feelings can be very strong motivating forces for change or momentum with a little bit of encouraging progress to help you believe that it is possible.

There was a nurse who came to Robin while she was studying for her master's degree in nursing at Vanderbilt University. So she already knew a lot about nutrition.

Robin said, "We started working together and discovered that as a child she was rewarded with food whether she was good or bad and she brought that into her adult life and was making poor choices. One of the things she had to do to improve her relationship with food was to address certain associations she had placed on food from when she was younger that she previously had no idea were affecting her health and her diet.

"One day we met at the grocery store to go shopping. I told her, 'Just do what you normally would and I'll do what I normally would.' When we were both done, she looked over at my shopping cart and said, 'There is no fun in your cart.' I had mostly greens in my cart because I love to juice. She had cupcakes, cookies and mostly boxed foods in her cart. I mentioned to her that when I looked in her cart there was no joy for me.

"I said to her, 'You're going shopping and you're picking out the food for yourself. If you saw a mom put the same food in her shopping cart and take it home for her child, what would you think? You're smart, you're a nurse. What do you want for your future? Do you want to walk hand in hand on the beach with someone you love when you are older or do you want to be sitting in a wheelchair?' Speed up the story. She has improved her relationship with food, is eating healthier and is now a practicing nurse setting great examples for her patients."

Robin encouraged me, "Don't just listen to what I'm saying, do some of your own research, and watch some of the health videos that are out there.

"The journey for every person I've talked to has never been the same. You can't just have one program or one solution for people to follow and think that is going to work long term.

"I'd rather invest my money into things I enjoy eating now rather than into medical bills later on. I want to be around."

What's your reason to change? Why do you want to expand your diet and no longer be an extremely picky eater? Why do you want to be healthier?

If you want to help someone change, you have to help them discover their reason for change. Find out what motivates them, what they love, what their purpose is or what matters to them enough for them to want to change. Then make it as simple as possible to start.

Picky Points:

- The number one reason people change is for something other than themselves.
- Your feelings, shared beliefs, and encouraging progress are strong motivating forces for change.
- Discover your reason for change and understand how motivation works.
- Help others discover their why.

RECIPE

GNOCCHI

—

Last but not least is our gnocchi. We are now taking our potato and making something that looks completely different with it. We are changing both the taste and texture to create something similar to a pasta. We are going to boil the potato again, in fact, we are going to boil it twice to create our gnocchi! The crunchy crisp texture is long gone replaced by a soft, plump, pillowy texture and a milder potato taste. You can change the taste quite a bit and add another texture component with any sauces that you introduce. Although it is also great with just a simple butter sauce and some parmesan cheese to start.

INGREDIENTS

- 2 Russet Potatoes
- 1/4 cup Egg
- 1 cup of Unbleached All-Purpose Flour
- Fine Grain Sea Salt

INSTRUCTIONS

1. Fill a large pot with cold water. Salt the water, and then cut potatoes in half and place them in the pot. Bring the water to a boil and cook the potatoes until tender throughout. This takes roughly 40-50 minutes.

2. Remove the potatoes from the water one at a time with a slotted spoon. Place each potato piece on a large cutting board and peel it. Save the potato water. Also, peel each potato as soon as possible after removing from the water (without burning yourself). I've found a paring knife comes in handy here. Be mindful that you want to work relatively quickly so you can mash the potatoes when they are hot. To do this you can either push the potatoes through a ricer, or do what I do, deconstruct them one at a time on the cutting board using the tines of a fork. Mash isn't quite the right term here. I run the fork down the sides of the peeled potato creating a nice, fluffy potato base to work with. Don't over mash. You are simply after an even consistency with no noticeable lumps.

3. Let the potatoes cool spread out across the cutting board—10 or 15 minutes. Long enough that the egg won't cook when it is incorporated into the potatoes. Lightly beat the egg.

4. When you're ready, pull the potatoes into a soft mound. Drizzle with the beaten egg and sprinkle 3/4 cup of the flour across the top. I've found that a metal spatula or large pastry scraper are both great utensils to use to incorporate the flour and eggs into the potatoes with the egg incorporated throughout. You can see the hint of yellow from the yolk. Scrape underneath and fold, scrape and fold until the mixture is a light crumble. Very gently, with a feathery touch, knead the dough. This is also the point you can add more flour (a sprinkle at a time) if the dough is too tacky. I usually end up using most of the remaining 1/4 cup flour, but it all depends on the potatoes, the flour, the time of year, the weather, and whether the gnocchi gods are smiling on you. The dough should be moist but not sticky. It should feel almost billowy.

5. Cut it into 8 pieces. Now gently roll each 1/8th of dough into a snake-shaped log, roughly the thickness of your thumb. Use a knife to cut pieces every 3/4-inch. Dust with a bit more flour.

6. To shape the gnocchi, hold a fork in one hand and place a gnocchi pillow against the tines of the fork (or gnocchi board), cut ends out. With confidence and an assertive (but very light) touch, use your thumb and press in and down the length of the fork. The gnocchi should curl into a slight "C" shape, their backs will capture the impression of the tines as tiny ridges (good for catching sauce later). Set each gnocchi aside. Dust with a bit more flour, if needed, until you are ready to boil them. This step takes some practice. Don't get discouraged. Once you get the hang of it it's easy.

7. Now that you're on the final stretch, either reheat your potato water or start with a fresh pot (salted), and bring to a boil. Cook the gnocchi in batches by dropping them into the boiling water roughly twenty at a time. They will let you know when they are cooked because they will pop back up to the top. Fish them out of the water a few at a time with a slotted spoon ten seconds or so after they've surfaced. Have a large platter ready with a generous swirl of whatever sauce or favorite pesto you'll be serving on the gnocchi. Place the gnocchi on the platter. Continue cooking in batches until all the gnocchi are done. Gently toss with more sauce or pesto (Don't overdo it. You could even just use a light butter sauce), and serve immediately, family-style with a drizzle of good olive oil and parmesan on top. Enjoy!

CONCLUSION

To wrap up let's begin with a personal note from my mom. "To this day I cannot believe my daughter now eats everything from pizza to sushi; the immense happiness and sense of pride this has brought to me and Jessica's dad cannot be measured! My daughter now tells me what the best method is for cooking moist fluffy scrambled eggs—not in a frying pan, but in a small sauce pan, periodically removing it from the heat as you stir. Absolutely amazing. I will also be eternally grateful to Felix Economakis for opening her eyes, heart and mind to the joy of eating different foods."~Judy Rohrer

I thought I would be an extremely picky eater for my entire life. I didn't believe I'd ever be able to get over my picky eating. For goodness' sakes, I didn't believe I'd ever be able to eat a chicken nugget! To say I never dreamed I'd write a book about food is a bit of an understatement!

It's been a long, and challenging journey—one that neither I nor my parents ever really understood until now. I am so incredibly grateful that I am no longer scared of food and I can now try a bite of anything. I never dreamed I'd be lucky enough to have the entire food world available to explore and that I'd experience so many incredible new tastes and textures. It has been absolutely amzing and has changed my world. The beauty is… it's still just the beginning and my relationship with food will continue to grow and evolve the rest of my life.

I hope that with this book I've been able to bring some small amount of awareness to your relationship with food and picky eating.

I will be more than thrilled if I've been able…to help you see that everyone's relationship with food is completely unique…to let you know you are not alone if you are currently struggling with your relationship with food…to help you take the very first step in changing your food habits… to give you hope that it is absolutely possible to change…or maybe, just maybe, to help even one picky eater overcome their food phobia.

Remember, anything is possible if you set your mind to it! Thank you so much for letting me share my life, my story, and my experiences with you, and I wish you all the very best on your journey with food. Good luck and God bless.

ACKNOWLEDGEMENT

—

First and foremost, I'd like to thank my family. Mom, Dad, Nelly, Mandy and Meg, thank you for the unwavering support and love, I wouldn't be the person I am today without you. Mom, thank you for defending me time and time again, making countless peanut butter and jelly sandwiches and for always reassuring me that everything would be okay. Dad, thank you for believing in me and seeing my potential even when I was unable to. Nelly & Mandy & Meg thank you for being the best sisters and friends anyone could ever ask for. I know I can always count on you, thank you for always being there for me. To my entire family, thank you for loving me just the way I am, even when that wasn't easy. I love you all so much.

Thank you to my Oakton High School friends. Thank you for standing by me year after year and cheering me on in all my endeavors. I'm forever grateful that we've maintained our strong friendships though college, jobs, busy lives, and different cities all these years. Thank you for picking restaurants I could eat at, providing Jessie snacks at parties and for accepting me and my picky eating.

Thank you to my friends in Brussels and in Nashville. Thank you for trying new foods with me at restaurants and making me feel welcome at Thanksgiving. Thank you for brainstorming with me, encouraging me, and allowing me to share my joys and frustrations with you throughout the book writing process. Special thank you to Wes for taking my awesome cover photos.

Thank you to all my interviewees. Thank you for taking time out of your busy schedules to sit down and talk to me about your experiences. This book just wouldn't be the same without your incredible stories.

Lastly a huge thank you to all the incredible people at New Degree Press for helping me spread the word about picky eating and turn this book into a reality.

Thank you.

RECIPES

———

CRISPY HOME FRIES

INGREDIENTS

- 1 Russet Potato
- 1 tablespoon Olive Oil
- Salt
- Pepper
- Garlic Powder

INSTRUCTIONS

1. Heat oven at 450°F. Put an aluminum foil covered pan in the oven as it heats up.
2. Peel potato, cut into small pieces.

3. Boil potatoes for 5–10 minutes until it is just about cooked through when you poke it with a fork and it starts to give.

4. Drain and dry the potatoes.

5. Dry them again. You want them as dry as possible.

6. Put them in a bowl. Add olive oil, salt, pepper and garlic powder and mix together coating potatoes.

7. Take the pan out of the oven. Spread the potatoes out on the aluminum covered pan with lots of space so they aren't touching.

8. Pop in the oven and roast for 10–15 minutes on one side.

9. Take them out and turn them.

10. Roast for another 10–15 minutes on another side.

11. Take them out when they've turned light brown and crispy. Enjoy!

SWEET POTATO FRIES

INGREDIENTS

- 1 pound Sweet Potatoes
- 2 tablespoons Cornstarch
- 1/2 teaspoon Kosher Salt
- 3 tablespoons Vegetable Oil

INSTRUCTIONS

1. Heat the oven to 400°F. Arrange two racks to divide the oven into thirds. Line two rimmed baking sheets with parchment paper if desired.
2. Peel the sweet potatoes. Cut in half lengthwise. Turn onto the cut side, then cut lengthwise into 1/4-inch wide planks. Lay the planks flat and cut lengthwise into 1/4-inch-thick sticks or wedges.
3. Place the sweet potato in a large zip-top plastic bag or bowl, add the cornstarch and salt, and shake or toss to combine until all the starch is absorbed into the sweet potato.
4. Coat the sweet potato in oil.
5. Divide the sweet potato among the 2 baking sheets and spread into a single, even layer, leaving space around each fry.
6. Roast until some of the fries are just starting to brown around the edges, about fifteen minutes. Remove the baking sheets from the oven. Using a flat spatula or turner, flip the sweet potatoes. Place back in the oven, switching the sheets between

racks, and continue to roast until the fries are tender on the inside and crispy on the outside, five to fifteen minutes more. They will crisp up a little more as they cool.

7.   Season with more salt if desired and serve.

HASH BROWNS

INGREDIENTS

- 3 Russet Potatoes
- 4 tablespoon Butter
- Salt
- Pepper

INSTRUCTIONS

1. Scrub potatoes (no need to peel or remove brown spots) and place in stockpot.
2. Cover the potatoes with cold, salted water and then bring to a boil.
3. Boil for about 10 minutes.
4. Drain and rinse potatoes with cold water until easy to handle. Remove any bruised or brown spots with a knife.
5. Using a box shredder or food processor, shred potatoes.
6. Melt butter in a large skillet or griddle over medium-heat (on the griddle we did 350°F).
7. Place potatoes evenly over the butter and cook until a golden-brown crust forms on the bottom (5-7 minutes). Flip potatoes and cook until crust forms on the other side.
8. Remove from heat and serve immediately.

POTATO PANCAKES

INGREDIENTS

- 1 Baking Potato
- 1 Egg
- 1/2 White Onion
- 1/4 cup of Milk or Cream
- 2 tablespoon of Parsley Flakes
- 1/2 cup Flour
- Salt
- Pepper

INSTRUCTIONS

1. Wash and dry the potato.
2. Cut into smaller pieces.
3. Blend potato, egg, onion, milk, parsley, salt and pepper together.
4. Pour in a bowl and add 1/4 cup of flour.
5. Heat up vegetable oil, duck fat or canola oil in a frying pan so it's sizzling.
6. Take a spoonful of the potato pancake mixture and drop into the pan to create pancakes.
7. Fry them until they are golden and crispy on each side.
8. Add a little salt on top when you take them out and enjoy!

BAKED POTATO

INGREDIENTS

- 4 Russet Potatoes
- 1/4 cup Olive Oil
- Butter
- Salt
- Pepper

INSTRUCTIONS

1. Heat the oven to 425°F.
2. Wash and dry the potatoes.
3. Pierce each potato 2–3 times with a fork.
4. Rub oil all over the potatoes.
5. Rub salt all over the potatoes.
6. Place the potatoes on a baking sheet and bake for about 45 minutes to an hour. The exact baking time will depend on how large the potatoes are. The potato should be tender inside if you poke a fork into it.
7. Serve with butter, salt, pepper, cheese, chives, sour cream and all of your favorite toppings!

FOR A FUN TWIST ON A BAKED POTATO, ADD A FEW ADDITIONAL STEPS AND TRY A HASSELBACK BAKED POTATO.

INSTRUCTIONS

1. Heat the oven to 425°F with a rack in the lower-middle position.
2. Wash and dry the potatoes.
3. Cut slits into the potato, stopping just before you cut through so that the slices stay connected at the bottom of the potato. Space the slices 1/8-inch to 1/4-inch apart. You can rest the potato in a large serving spoon and use that as a guide for when to stop slicing. Slice straight down and when your knife hits the edge of the spoon, stop slicing.
4. Brush the potatoes with olive oil.
5. Sprinkle with salt and pepper.
6. Bake 30 minutes, then nudge layers apart and brush with butter.
7. Bake another 30 to 40 minutes until the potatoes are crispy on the edges and easily pierced in the middles with *a paring knife.*
8. If you're adding any extras, (cheese, sour cream, bacon, minced herbs) stuff those into the slits and sprinkle over the top 5 to 10 minutes before the end of cooking.
9. Serve immediately: These potatoes are best straight from the oven while the edges are at their crispiest.
10. Add a little salt on top when you take them out.

MASHED POTATOES

INGREDIENTS

- 2 pounds Russet Potatoes
- 2 tablespoons Butter
- 1 cup Milk
- Salt
- Pepper

INSTRUCTIONS

1. Bring a pot of salted water to a boil.
2. Peel your potatoes and quarter them.
3. Add potatoes and cook until tender but still firm for about 15 minutes.
4. Drain the water from your pot.
5. In a small saucepan heat butter and milk over low heat until butter is melted.
6. Using a potato masher or electric beater, slowly blend milk mixture into potatoes until smooth and creamy
7. Season with salt and pepper to taste.

GNOCCHI

INGREDIENTS

- 2 Russet Potatoes
- 1/4 cup Egg
- 1 cup of Unbleached All-Purpose Flour
- Fine Grain Sea Salt

INSTRUCTIONS

1. Fill a large pot with cold water. Salt the water, and then cut potatoes in half and place them in the pot. Bring the water to a boil and cook the potatoes until tender throughout. This takes roughly 40-50 minutes.

2. Remove the potatoes from the water one at a time with a slotted spoon. Place each potato piece on a large cutting board and peel it. Save the potato water. Also, peel each potato as soon as possible after removing from the water (without burning yourself). I've found a paring knife comes in handy here. Be mindful that you want to work relatively quickly so you can mash the potatoes when they are hot. To do this you can either push the potatoes through a ricer, or do what I do, deconstruct them one at a time on the cutting board using the tines of a fork. Mash isn't quite the right term here. I run the fork down the sides of the peeled potato creating a nice, fluffy potato base to work with. Don't over mash. You are simply after an even consistency with no noticeable lumps.

3. Let the potatoes cool spread out across the cutting board—10 or 15 minutes. Long enough that the egg won't cook when it is incorporated into the potatoes. Lightly beat the egg.

4. When you're ready, pull the potatoes into a soft mound. Drizzle with the beaten egg and sprinkle 3/4 cup of the flour across the top. I've found that a metal spatula or large pastry scraper are both great utensils to use to incorporate the flour and eggs into the potatoes with the egg incorporated throughout. You can see the hint of yellow from the yolk. Scrape underneath and fold, scrape and fold until the mixture is a light crumble. Very gently, with a feathery touch, knead the dough. This is also the point you can add more flour (a sprinkle at a time) if the dough is too tacky. I usually end up using most of the remaining 1/4 cup flour, but it all depends on the potatoes, the flour, the time of year, the weather, and whether the gnocchi gods are smiling on you. The dough should be moist but not sticky. It should feel almost billowy.

5. Cut it into 8 pieces. Now gently roll each 1/8th of dough into a snake-shaped log, roughly the thickness of your thumb. Use a knife to cut pieces every 3/4-inch. Dust with a bit more flour.

6. To shape the gnocchi, hold a fork in one hand and place a gnocchi pillow against the tines of the fork (or gnocchi board), cut ends out. With confidence and an assertive (but very light) touch, use your thumb and press in and down the length of the fork. The gnocchi should curl into a slight "C" shape, their backs will capture the impression of the tines as tiny ridges (good for catching sauce later). Set each gnocchi aside. Dust

with a bit more flour, if needed, until you are ready to boil them. This step takes some practice. Don't get discouraged. Once you get the hang of it it's easy.

7. Now that you're on the final stretch, either reheat your potato water or start with a fresh pot (salted), and bring to a boil. Cook the gnocchi in batches by dropping them into the boiling water roughly twenty at a time. They will let you know when they are cooked because they will pop back up to the top. Fish them out of the water a few at a time with a slotted spoon ten seconds or so after they've surfaced. Have a large platter ready with a generous swirl of whatever sauce or favorite pesto you'll be serving on the gnocchi. Place the gnocchi on the platter. Continue cooking in batches until all the gnocchi are done. Gently toss with more sauce or pesto (Don't overdo it. You can also use a light butter sauce), and serve immediately, family-style with a drizzle of good olive oil and parmesan cheese on top. Enjoy!

CITATIONS

———

INTRODUCTION

Eatingrecoverycenter.com. (2019). *Picky Eating vs. Disordered Eating (ARFID) Signs & Symptoms | Eating Recovery Center.* [online] Available at: https://www.eatingrecoverycenter.com/families/portal/resource-center/where-does-picky-eating-end-and-disordered-eating [Accessed 12 Jan. 2019].

Norris, M., Spettigue, W. and Katzman, D. (2016). Update on eating disorders: current perspectives on avoidant/restrictive food intake disorder in children and youth. *Neuropsychiatric Disease and Treatment*, p.213.

Statista. (2015). *Which of the following people, if any, do you consider to be picky eaters?* [online] Available at: https://www.statista.

com/statistics/426021/picky-eaters-in-the-united-states/ [Accessed 12 Jan. 2019].

PART 1: WHAT IS PICKY EATING

Anxiety.org. (2019). *Phobias.* [online] Available at: https://www. anxiety.org/phobias [Accessed 12 Jan. 2019].

Economakis, F. (2016). *Top Six Myths About Selective Eating Disorder (food phobias).* [online] YourTango. Available at: https:// www.yourtango.com/experts/felixeconomakis/top-six-myths-about-selective-eating-disorder-food-phobias/ [Accessed 12 Jan. 2019].

Grogan, A. (2013). *Has Picky Eating Gone Too Far: Food Aversion Disorders in Kids.* [online] Your Kid's Table. Available at: https://yourkidstable.com/picky-eating-vs-problem-feeder/ [Accessed 12 Jan. 2019].

Toomey, K. (2010). *Picky Eaters vs. Problem Feeders | SOS Approach to Feeding.* [online] Sosapproach-conferences.com. Available at: http://sosapproach-conferences.com/resources/picky-eaters-vs-problem-feeders/ [Accessed 12 Jan. 2019].

Toomey, K. (2010). *When Children Won't Eat: Understanding the "Why's" and How to Help.*

PART 2: EXPOSURE AND INVOLVEMENT

Bennington-Castro, J. (2013). *The Psychology of Hating Food (and How We Learn to Love It)*. [online] I09.gizmodo.com. Available at: https://i09.gizmodo.com/the-psychology-of-hating-food-and-how-we-learn-to-love-476720251 [Accessed 12 Jan. 2019].

Birch, L., McPhee, L., Shoba, B., Pirok, E. and Steinberg, L. (2006). What kind of exposure reduces children's food neophobia?: Looking vs. tasting. *ScienceDirect*, [online] 9(3), pp.171-178. Available at: http://www.sciencedirect.com.

Christians, L. (2015). *Eating is a learned behavior. Ruth Reichl talks food criticism, 'kids food' and what we throw away*. [online] Madison.com. Available at: https://madison.com/ct/entertainment/dining/eating-is-a-learned-behavior-ruth-reichl-talks-food-criticism/article_6e78e9db-3cfe-51d6-b92c-31944d09c853.html [Accessed 12 Jan. 2019].

Dewar, G. (2009). *The science of picky eaters: Why do children reject foods that we find tasty?* [online] Parentingscience.com. Available at: https://www.parentingscience.com/picky-eaters.html [Accessed 12 Jan. 2019].

PART 3: WHAT TO DO AND MODELING

Becker, A., Burwell, R., Herzog, D., Hamburg, P. and Gilman, S. (2002). Eating behaviours and attitudes following prolonged exposure to television among ethnic Fijian adolescent girls. *British Journal of Psychiatry*, 180(06), pp.509-514.

Fishbein, M., Cox, S., Swenny, C., Mogren, C., Walbert, L. and Fraker, C. (2006). Food Chaining: A Systematic Approach for the Treatment of Children With Feeding Aversion. *Nutrition in Clinical Practice*, 21(2), pp.182-184.

Michels, N., Sioen, I., Braet, C., Eiben, G., Hebestreit, A., Huybrechts, I., Vanaelst, B., Vyncke, K. and De Henauw, S. (2012). Stress, emotional eating behaviour and dietary patterns in children. *Appetite*, 59(3), pp.762-769.

Stulberg, B. (2014). *The Key to Changing Individual Health Behaviors: Change the Environments That Give Rise to Them | Harvard Public Health Review: A Student Publication.* [online] Harvardpublichealthreview.org. Available at: http://harvardpublichealthreview.org/the-key-to-changing-individual-health-behaviors-change-the-environments-that-give-rise-to-them/ [Accessed 12 Jan. 2019].

Wansink, B. and Kim, J. (2005). Bad Popcorn in Big Buckets: Portion Size Can Influence Intake as Much as Taste. *Journal of Nutrition Education and Behavior*, 37(5), pp.242-245.

Wansink, B., Painter, J. and North, J. (2005). Bottomless Bowls: Why Visual Cues of Portion Size May Influence Intake**. *Obesity Research*, 13(1), pp.93-100.

Wright, J. (2017). *Father's Day PSA: your kids are what you eat.* [online] CBC News. Available at: https://www.cbc.ca/news/canada/new-brunswick/dads-eating-habits-1.4161796 [Accessed 12 Jan. 2019].

Yau, Y. and Potenza, M. (2013). *Stress and Eating Behaviors.* [online] PubMed Central (PMC). Available at: https://www.ncbi.nlm.nih.gov/pmc/articles/PMC4214609/#R20 [Accessed 12 Jan. 2019].

PART 4: LEARN ABOUT FOOD AND COOKING

Choi, A. (2014). *What Americans can learn from other food cultures.* [online] ideas.ted.com. Available at: https://ideas.ted.com/what-americans-can-learn-from-other-food-cultures/ [Accessed 12 Jan. 2019].

Hamm, T. (2017). *Don't Eat Out as Often (188/365) - The Simple Dollar.* [online] The Simple Dollar. Available at: https://www.thesimpledollar.com/dont-eat-out-as-often-188365/ [Accessed 12 Jan. 2019].

PART 5: OUR RELATIONSHIPS WITH FOOD

Arond, M. (2014). The Power of Food: Belief vs. Reality. [online] HuffPost. Available at: https://www.huffpost.com/entry/the-power-of-food-belief_b_6037176 [Accessed 15 Jan. 2019].

Birch, L., Savage, J. and Ventura, A. (2007). Influence on the Development of Children's Eating Behaviors: From Infancy to Adolescence. *Can J Diet Pract Res*, [online] 68. Available at: https://www.ncbi.nlm.nih.gov/pmc/articles/PMC2678872/ [Accessed 12 Jan. 2019].

Bjarnadottir, A. (2017). *The 18 Most Addictive Foods (and the 17 Least Addictive)*. [online] Healthline. Available at: https://www.healthline.com/nutrition/18-most-addictive-foods [Accessed 12 Jan. 2019].

Denton, C. (2016). *How Does Food Impact Health? | Taking Charge of Your Health & Wellbeing*. [online] Taking Charge of Your Health & Wellbeing. Available at: https://www.takingcharge.csh.umn.edu/explore-healing-practices/food-medicine/how-does-food-impact-health [Accessed 12 Jan. 2019].

Eating Disorders on the College Campus. (2013). [ebook] National Eating Disorder Association, pp.5-35. Available at: https://www.nationaleatingdisorders.org/sites/default/files/CollegeSurvey/CollegiateSurveyProject.pdf [Accessed 12 Jan. 2019].

Fields, R. (2011). *The Deadliest Disorder*. [online] Psychology Today. Available at: https://www.psychologytoday.com/us/blog/the-new-brain/201103/the-deadliest-disorder-0 [Accessed 12 Jan. 2019].

ReShel, A. (2017). *The Relationship Between Food and Emotions*. [online] UPLIFT. Available at: https://upliftconnect.com/relationship-between-food-and-emotions/ [Accessed 12 Jan. 2019].

Savage, J., Fisher, J. and Birch, L. (2007). Parental Influence on Eating Behavior: Conception to Adolescence. *The Journal of Law, Medicine & Ethics*, 35(1), pp.22-34.

Tartakovsky, M. (2018). *What Is Normal Eating?*. [online] World of Psychology. Available at: https://psychcentral.com/blog/what-is-normal-eating/ [Accessed 12 Jan. 2019].

PART 6: WHAT NOT TO DO

Adler, L. and Bass, P. (2019). *Why Parents Shouldn't Use Food as Reward or Punishment - Health Encyclopedia - University of Rochester Medical Center*. [online] Urmc.rochester.edu. Available at: https://www.urmc.rochester.edu/encyclopedia/content.aspx?ContentTypeID=160&ContentID=32 [Accessed 12 Jan. 2019].

Friedman, H. and Martin, L. (2012). The Longevity Project: Surprising Discoveries for Health and Long Life from the Landmark Eight-Decade Study. *Population and Development Review*, 38(1), pp.175-176.

Gunnars, K. (2018). *Protein Intake – How Much Protein Should You Eat Per Day?* [online] Healthline. Available at: https://www.healthline.com/nutrition/how-much-protein-per-day [Accessed 12 Jan. 2019].

Novotney, A. (2011). *The real secrets to a longer life.* [online] http://www.apa.org. Available at: https://www.apa.org/monitor/2011/12/longer-life.aspx [Accessed 12 Jan. 2019].

NPR.org. (2011). *Secrets To Longevity: It's Not All About Broccoli.* [online] Available at: https://www.npr.org/2011/03/24/134827587/secrets-to-longevity-its-not-all-about-broccoli [Accessed 12 Jan. 2019].

Weiss, L. (2013). *Nutrition expert: Kids shouldn't be forced to clean their plates.* [online] Digitaljournal.com. Available at: http://www.digitaljournal.com/article/355871#ixzz5bmcSxUNr [Accessed 12 Jan. 2019].

PART 7: AWARENESS AND CHANGE

Brilaki, M. (2017). *How Many Days Does It Take To Form A Habit? 'Not 21,' Science Says.* [online] Fitness Reloaded. Available at:

https://fitnessreloaded.com/how-many-days-to-form-a-habit/ [Accessed 12 Jan. 2019].

GRAINSTORM. (2019). *What's wrong with modern wheat.* [online] Available at: https://grainstorm.com/pages/modern-wheat [Accessed 12 Jan. 2019].

Greco, L., Gobbetti, M., Auricchio, R., Di Mase, R., Landolfo, F., Paparo, F., Di Cagno, R., De Angelis, M., Rizzello, C., Cassone, A., Terrone, G., Timpone, L., D'Aniello, M., Maglio, M., Troncone, R. and Auricchio, S. (2011). Safety for Patients With Celiac Disease of Baked Goods Made of Wheat Flour Hydrolyzed During Food Processing. *Clinical Gastroenterology and Hepatology*, 9(1), pp.24-29.

Miller, C. (2017). *Changing Your Habits for Better Health | NIDDK.* [online] National Institute of Diabetes and Digestive and Kidney Diseases. Available at: https://www.niddk.nih.gov/health-information/diet-nutrition/changing-habits-better-health [Accessed 12 Jan. 2019].

Sass, C. (2014). *6 Fascinating Things a Food Journal Can Teach You About Your Eating Habits.* [online] Health. Available at: https://www.health.com/nutrition/6-fascinating-things-a-food-journal-can-teach-you-about-your-eating-habits [Accessed 12 Jan. 2019].

Made in the USA
Middletown, DE
27 February 2019